MAGNETS:
The Education of a Physicist

PROFESSOR FRANCIS BITTER was born in Weehawken, New Jersey, in 1902 and spent his childhood in New York City. He was graduated from Columbia College in 1924, studied physics in Berlin in 1925–26, and received his Ph.D. at Columbia in 1929. Following research on the magnetic properties of gases at California Institute of Technology, he joined the research staff of Westinghouse Electric and Manufacturing Company in Pittsburgh, exploring both theoretical and applied problems in magnetism. He joined the faculty of Massachusetts Institute of Technology in 1934 and developed extremely powerful magnets for various studies of the magnetic nature of matter. Dr. Bitter spent the war years with the U. S. Navy, working on problems of magnetic mines and how ships could be made less susceptible to them. A professor of physics at M.I.T. since 1950, Dr. Bitter has recently investigated the magnetic aspects of the nuclei of atoms.

MAGNETS:

THE EDUCATION
OF A PHYSICIST

by Francis Bitter

Published by
Doubleday Anchor Books
Doubleday & Company, Inc.
Garden City, New York
1959

Available to secondary
school students and teachers through
Wesleyan University Press Incorporated
Columbus 16, Ohio

COVER DESIGN BY GEORGE GIUSTI
ILLUSTRATIONS BY R. PAUL LARKIN

Library of Congress Catalog Card Number 59–9611

THE SCIENCE STUDY SERIES

The Science Study Series offers to students and to the general public the writing of distinguished authors on the most stirring and fundamental topics of physics, from the smallest known particles to the whole universe. Some of the books tell of the role of physics in the world of man, his technology and his civilization. Others are biographical in nature, telling the fascinating stories of the great discoverers and their discoveries. All the authors have been selected both for expertness in the fields they discuss and for ability to communicate their special knowledge and their own views in an interesting way. The primary purpose of these books is to provide a survey of physics within the grasp of the young student or the layman. Many of the books, it is hoped, will encourage the reader to make his own investigations of natural phenomena.

These books are published as a part of a fresh approach to the teaching and study of physics. At the Massachusetts Institute of Technology during 1956 a group of physicists, high school teachers, journalists, apparatus designers, film producers, and other specialists organized the Physical Science Study Committee, now operating as a part of Educational Services Incorporated, Watertown, Massachusetts. They pooled their knowledge and experience toward the design and creation of aids to the learning of physics.

8

CONTENTS

Contents

A NOTE BEFORE YOU BEGIN

Science is a world with many fields to be explored. One of these is magnetism—a subject dealing with one of the many influences that one bit of matter can exert on another. We know as much about magnetism as about anything else in this world—or in this universe, for that matter. But when it comes right down to it, we have not scratched the surface, not to any depth, in perceiving the true relationship of this to other kinds of influences that can be exerted from here to there across empty space—nor in breadth, in realizing the complexity of the magnetic interplay of electronic winds as they blow through outer space, or around the atoms, or even through the lamps and tubes we make and use and accept as trivial in our daily lives.

I shall tell you about magnetism in the most valid way I know—and in an interesting way, I hope—by describing my personal voyage of exploration, and how it felt to me. As you read, you will learn a little bit about magnetism. You will not learn as much as you would from a long and detailed study of the facts. But you will learn *something* about magnetism, and perhaps quite a lot of a man's life and his absorption in his work. My work (it might better be called my fun) always has been concerned with magnetism. How did it begin? It began as it always must, by learning a language. It began with hard work and drudgery as well as fun and excitement; by my learning many lessons—for example, this one in my college days.

Science and mathematics were easy for me. I did not have to work very hard to get by. My family was not well off, but even in those days, before easy fellowship support, I was able to borrow money to see me through college. One day I saw a notice of a competition for a cash prize to be awarded for excellence in applied mathematics. If I should win that, it would be a most welcome addition to my pocket money. I took the competitive exam, and I still remember the cocky feeling I had when I looked around and saw no one I considered a serious rival. I was very confident. But when the results were announced, it was not I who had won. It was an unknown. Someone who had not become a member of the discussion groups, the bull sessions, the argumentative lunch clubs, just someone who was quiet and smart.

As I now think back on this time, I am reminded of a children's party that my wife gave recently. One boy was somewhat older than the rest. He was rather disdainful and obviously felt superior. Toward the end of the party we had a competition—to see who was best at tossing cards into a hat. It looked easy. The various children tried with negligible success. At last it was the turn of the older boy. He strutted up and obviously expected every card to land in the hat. The first went wild. He looked sheepish. The second went wild. He looked embarrassed. The third, fourth, and fifth he threw in rapid succession, but all missed. With a bewildered look he turned to us and said, "Hey, what's wrong?"

That was just my feeling when I failed to win the competition—"Hey, what's wrong?" I had not yet learned that singlehearted hard work and devotion and even love were necessary for any *success,* for any real achievement. If these ingredients are not there, one cannot contribute or benefit as one might. It was a good lesson to learn at the very beginning of my career. And there were many more.

But let us start at the beginning—learning the language of science. Let me tell you something of what I learned, and why it fascinated me.

MAGNETS:
The Education of a Physicist

CHAPTER I

Learning the Language

My interest in magnetism began with my second try at a Ph.D. thesis. In those days at Columbia University you chose a thesis topic, then you tried to find a professor who was willing to supervise this thesis, and finally arrangements were made for you to have space in one of the research rooms. You were then off on your own in your first independent investigation. At that time I had just discovered a lengthy publication on the subject of my first proposed thesis. This was rather a calamity, since a thesis is presumed to contain original work, and here I had discovered that the work I proposed to do had already been done. Six months of effort seemed wasted. As I was walking rather disconsolately around the corridors wondering how one ever got to know a subject well enough to be reasonably sure that any particular investigation had not just been completed in some remote corner of the world, my eye lit on an impressive-looking magnet in an empty laboratory.

For those days, the mid-1920's, this was a large and important-looking piece of equipment—five feet high, weighing several tons, I suspected, with heavy wires coming out of it, terminating in a husky switch. This sort of magnet was not a generally familiar sight. It was a research tool to create very strong fields in a small volume—for investigating subtle magnetic effects. It immediately caught my fancy. I went in to examine it.

But before we can step into the empty laboratory with the magnet in it and understand some of the thoughts that went through my head as I was groping for a new thesis topic, we must go back over a period of years and review some of the scientific language and some of the sights and ideas I had been taught. Before you can read or write stories you must learn spelling and grammar; before you can play a sonata on the piano you must learn scales, harmony, and musical notation; and before you can go into a laboratory and make an intelligent stab at discovering something new, there is a lot of dull, hard work to be done. No one escapes that. Some go through this learning more quickly than others; some mind it less because they are more aware of the approaching ability to think independently, but we must all learn what has been achieved by past masters in our field of work. We must submit to a new discipline.

BEFORE COLLEGE

What sort of a child is it who later becomes a physicist? Are there recognizable signs in childhood? I would say not. There is no rule to apply to sort out the scientist from the person who happily will pursue some other vocation. In my case I would say two qualities of character were important, and they have stayed with me through the years. One is imaginativeness. The other is an inquiring mind. Because I seldom accepted the statements or instructions of others, my family used to predict that I would become a lawyer. I would argue interminably, but the sorts of things that I argued about did not in the end center on legal matters. They centered on the description and understanding of the world around me.

One of my earliest recollections in this connection is of Sunday walks in New York City's Central Park, with my father wearing a high hat, my brother and sister and I in our Sunday best. Doubtless we discussed many different things on these sunny Sunday mornings, but I remember particularly the stories of the origin of the world—how rocks and the earth were formed, how living things appeared on the earth, eventually men like ourselves—and how cities grew. My father, a sculptor, was a great reader, and knew a good deal of natural history. His discourses fascinated me.

Life in our New York studio apartment was relatively uneventful. We children were brought up on a rather strict schedule. We learned and used three languages: German with our parents, French with a governess, and English in school. Piano lessons, dancing lessons, a little military drill with the Knickerbocker Greys in the Seventh Regiment Armory, visits to the Museum of Natural History on rainy days, reading "good" books on Sundays—such was the stuff of which our home life was made until, at twelve, I went to boarding school.

One of our favorite games was called *enfant perdu*

or "lost child." One of us pretended to be lost, destitute, deserted, in a completely hopeless situation, and another of us would find this lost waif. The foundling was adopted and gradually introduced to his or her "new" life. First we would exchange anecdotes about the real or imagined past. Then we would show off the magnificence of a New York elevator apartment, the "new" customs of the family, "new" foods at the table, "new" clothes and toys in our children's closets. The waif would be sent off to a "new" school, and our old friends would become his "new" friends.

The game took several days and, as I remember it, we played it not once but many times. It seems to me now that this may well have been an appropriate exercise for a future scientist. Scientific investigations are started and discoveries are made as the result of a repeated review of well-known facts, attempts to rearrange them, to see them from a new point of view that will excite new interest and reveal new possibilities. And this is just what we were doing in our children's world.

This *enfant perdu* game we played, as I remember it, when we were nine, ten, eleven years old. Another event that stands out in my mind must have happened in my early teens. I was paddling a canoe on a clear night and letting my thoughts roam. Suddenly it came over me, and with something of a shock, that maybe everything I considered most real was pure imagination. The lake, the canoe, the paddle, the stars, the night, the trees, even the feeling of water on my hand, might merely be sensations. Indeed, it might be that I was the only person who existed in the world, that my father and mother, my brother and sister and friends were all just figments of my own imagination—that the feeling of the solid earth when I walked on it was only a feeling. There seemed to be nothing to disprove the hypothesis. On the other hand, what would be the sense of such a thing? It occurred to me that possibly this was all a matter of education. Perhaps really I was not a young boy alive here on the world, but one of a group of other kinds of beings, perhaps a god or supernatural being of some sort who was merely going through a course of training prepared for him by other supernatural beings. At the time, no one seemed particularly interested in this form of nonsense, but when I studied philosophy in college it was somewhat of a thrill to realize that I was by no means the first to have considered the possibility.

At my high school the curriculum included no science whatever. We did have excellent courses in algebra and geometry, which I loved far above anything else. These subjects were easy for me and, if my recollection is right, I was one of the best students in the class. Solving problems by means of equations with unknowns, proving theorems on the basis of postulates—these were exciting, far more interesting than Latin and history, English and geography.

Presently I was ready for college. My grades in general had not been particularly good. On the other hand, I had never had to work particularly hard. Unlike many boys, I was not interested in wiring doorbells and building radios. Such pastimes seemed either boringly trivial or too complicated for me to understand. But when I entered college I had a notion—I remember it vividly—that I wanted to get to the bottom of certain kinds of magic; for example, I wanted to know what a magician did when he poured a liquid of one color into a liquid of another color and transformed it into a liquid of a third color. My first request on registering as a freshman at the University of Chicago was to be allowed to study chemistry in order to understand this. I was told that physics was a prerequisite for the chemistry courses. This prerequisite opened a very long detour for me. In fact, I never got around to studying the mysterious changing colors of chemical compounds. In all my university days I have had few chemistry courses. For me, it turned out, the physics courses were far more satisfying.

THE ABC'S OF SCIENCE

Learning physics in college was a peculiar mixture of tedious grind interspersed with a few fascinating discoveries. When you are eager, when you haunt the library in search of new facts or theories to enable you to continue a project of your own, learning is fun. But learning is not much fun when you are dealing with masses of definitions and new concepts, especially when the new ideas and new words seem strange and arbitrary, and when their use, even after you have learned the meaning, is nebulous.

To begin with, there was mechanics—the study of how things move, and under what conditions they will stand still. This may seem too trivial a subject to require much effort, and usually is so taught that students fail to see its scope and significance. Mechanics, after having been systematized and reformulated by great minds, is in fact one of the most satisfying, beautiful, and intricate subdivisions of physics. But most students, like myself, see something like this:

distance, inch, foot, mile, kilometer, meter, millimeter, centimeter, speed, velocity, miles per hour, cm/sec, acceleration, cm/sec^2, force, vector, lb, newton, Newton, statics, dynamics, mass, gm, mg, kg, slug, center of mass, center of percussion, angles, degrees, radians, impulse, angular momentum, centrifugal, centripetal, kinetic, potential, torques, sliding trunks, inclined planes, friction, static, bouncing balls, coefficient of restitution, moment of inertia, oscillation, pendulum, elasticity, simple harmonic motion, collisions, elastic, inelastic, First Law, Second Law, Third Law, Principles, Conservation, what is it, why, where, when, how, remember, tests, quizzes, exams, instruments, measurements, boredom, slump, headaches, sunshine and air, the bell . . . LET ME OUT!

After mechanics came the studies of heat, sound, light, and electricity and magnetism. Each has its own characteristic peculiarities, its own special complications, its own new ideas. For even a first superficial review of these subjects two or three years is not a long time.

What are the compensations for the drudgery of learning all the many facts? These compensations are, of course, different for different people. There is great satisfaction in the sense of achievement that comes with understanding something that seemed mysterious and inexplicable, and then in being able to use the new knowledge. Two examples stand out in my memory. The first had to do with heat flow. The problem which I am about to describe was taken up in a mathematics course, but its interest to me was entirely in relation to the actual physical situation it illustrates.

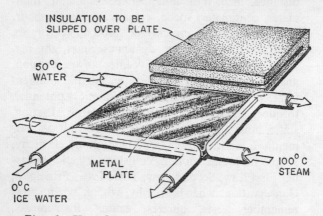

Fig. 1. Heat-flow problem, schematically shown here, was an early educational challenge. The mathematical goal is to calculate the temperature at any point on the metal plate.

A rectangular metal plate having specified properties is connected to arbitrary sources of heat and cold at its edges. For example, we might consider the plate sketched in Fig. 1, in which one edge is kept at 0° C, the adjacent edges at 50° and 100° respectively; the opposite edge is insulated, so that no heat flows across it. What is the temperature at every point of the plate? This seems a hopelessly complicated situation, but the solution, though lengthy, can be found. Further, once we have found the solution and made a contour map showing the temperature at ev-

ery point of the plate, as in Fig. 2, the solution
seems reasonable enough. The mystery is the method
of proceeding from ignorance to understanding.

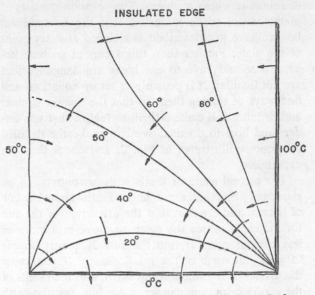

*Fig. 2. Contour map charts the solution of the
problem imagined in Fig. 1. Arrows show the direction of heat flow. The isothermal, or "contour,"
lines link points of equal temperature. Note that
heat flows "downhill."*

The whole trick is to consider a tiny little piece of
the plate in which the flow is in straight lines. In a
sufficiently small piece of the plate the heat flows in
just one direction, in a straight line from a hot "edge"
to a cool "edge," and the amount of heat that flows
from the hot to the cool edge in the tiny little element

25

of volume depends on this temperature difference, on the heat conductivity of the metal, and on the thickness of the plate. This is all the knowledge we need to solve the whole problem. The solution consists of mathematical tricks to insure that the fundamental law we have just described is satisfied at every point of the plate. Further than this I cannot go here because I should have to use ideas and language that are not familiar. It is possible to set up equations and find ways of solving them so that the answer is clear and definite. It is quite a thrill to realize that you understand how to do this. We can make the detailed predictions, illustrated in Fig. 2, and check them by experiment.*

The second example deals with astronomy. In an elementary mechanics course one learns about the law of gravity and the fact that the attraction of the sun for the earth causes the earth to move in a more or less circular orbit around the sun. It is very simple to work out some of the relationships. If you know the masses of the sun and the earth, and the radius of the earth's orbit, you can work out how fast the earth must move. The same ideas apply to the motion of the moon around the earth, or to the motion of any of the planets.

At the time I speak of, the theory of relativity was being widely discussed, and among the consequences of the theory of relativity were predictions of certain

*The check would be found satisfactory insofar as we could reproduce in an experiment the exact conditions assumed in the mathematical treatment. The reader might consider some of the practical difficulties to be expected in trying to check experimentally the correctness of the solution of the problem described.

deviations in the motion of the planet Mercury from the orbit that was to be expected on the simple Newtonian theory. A professor at Columbia was offering a course in celestial mechanics—the study of the motion of the planets in their orbits—and I enrolled for the course. The intention was to show how one could work through in detail the expected motions of the planets, taking into account not only the attraction of the sun, but also the small attractions of the planets for each other. This, it turned out, was not a popular course. In fact, I was the only student who registered that term. My recollection, however, is not only of the pleasure associated with discovering how to carry out a complicated procedure of this kind, but of seeing for myself how the predictions of the new and exciting theory of relativity were verified by observation. Since I was the only member of the class, the professor took liberties in straying from the announced program, and we spent more than half the time reviewing experimental facts which then did not completely satisfy my teacher.

We reviewed, among other matters, the experimental evidence for the gravitational attraction between the sun and a beam of light passing near it. This close look at the actual evolution of physics will also illustrate the kind of surprise that overtakes any wanderer far from home. Let us suppose a star is off in the direction specified by the ray at Point I in Fig. 3 and that when the earth is at this point an observer can fix this direction accurately with respect to all the other fixed stars. Now, six months later, when the earth in its orbit has arrived at Point II, light from the star must pass close to the sun to reach an ob-

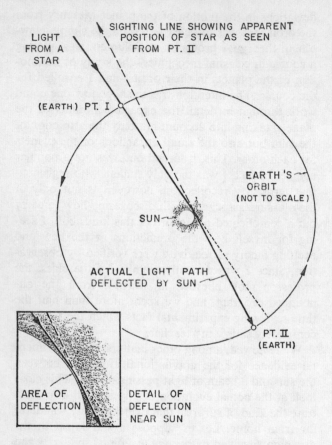

LIGHT
FROM A
STAR

SIGHTING LINE SHOWING APPARENT
POSITION OF STAR AS SEEN
FROM PT. II

(EARTH) PT. I

EARTH'S
ORBIT
(NOT TO SCALE)

SUN

ACTUAL LIGHT PATH
DEFLECTED BY SUN

PT. II
(EARTH)

AREA OF
DEFLECTION

DETAIL OF
DEFLECTION
NEAR SUN

Fig. 3. Sun's gravitational force bends light rays as they pass close to it. This deflection of light from a star causes an apparent shift in the star's position when viewed from opposite points on the earth's orbit. Albert Einstein predicted this phenomenon. Compare this illustration with Fig. 4.

server on the earth. In passing through the sun's gravitational field the light will be deflected. An observer will see the star in the direction of the deflected solid line at II rather than in the originally observed direction indicated by the dotted line at II. Under these conditions the star usually cannot be observed because of the brightness of the sun.

If, however, we have an eclipse, with the moon blocking off the sun's light, the star field near the sun can be photographed, and these photographs can be compared with the same field photographed from Point I. The theory of relativity predicted that a star field such as that shown in Fig. 4 as it appears from Point I should be modified as indicated by the arrows when photographed at Point II during an eclipse. The stars that appear at the base of the arrows in Fig. 4 when photographed from Point I were predicted to lie at the tips of the arrows in a photograph taken from Point II. What were the experimental facts? I expected a "confirmation" of the theory to show the stars exactly at the tips of the arrows. My professor showed me the results of actual experiment, illustrated in Fig. 4. At first it confused me. On the one hand, the theory of relativity was generally accepted as correct. On the other hand, the evidence for it seemed far from convincing. But a study of the experimental results made it clear that during an eclipse there were all kinds of small displacements of the stars that had nothing to do with the theory of relativity. Before any conclusions about the theory of relativity could be drawn, extensive corrections had to be made and the data analyzed statistically to determine whether there

29

were residual effects that could properly be attributed to the sun's attraction for light.

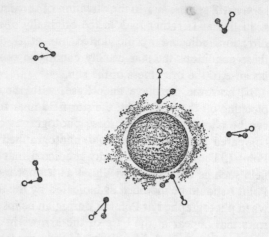

● POSITION SEEN FROM PT. I

○ THEORETICAL POSITION FROM PT. II

◉ OBSERVED POSITION FROM PT. II DURING ECLIPSE OF SUN

Fig. 4. In an eclipse of the sun the stellar shift can be observed. The difference in the predicted and observed displacements is shown by the dark and light circles. The discrepancy is due to irregularities in the bending of light rays in the atmosphere.

It then began to dawn on me that scientific exploration of unknown fields might be very much like geographic exploration in a fog. The investigator is looking for something that never has been seen, and he must expect to discover something barely discernible at first. If it could be seen clearly and distinctly with existing equipment it would have been discovered long ago. He must learn to look very carefully, and to distinguish real objects from accidentally occurring wisps of denser fog. Usually it is only later, after extensive work and the development of new apparatus and methods, that he will be able to approach the object of his search from many sides and see it clearly. To the expert, however, the first glimpses may be completely satisfying and conclusive, as was the case for the astronomers who carefully examined and interpreted the stellar displacements near the sun during an eclipse.

These were some of the experiences that fascinated me and made me anxious to continue my study of science. As you see, like any other student, I had to learn many branches of the subject. Out of these studies gradually evolved my principal preoccupation with one particular subject—namely magnetism. In the next chapter is a description, as I remember it, of the first things that I learned about magnetism. From this beginning I went on in later parts of my life to new aspects of the subject and a new insight into its relationship to the world around me.

CHAPTER II

Magnetism—and Electricity

Probably every reader has some vague idea of what we mean by a magnet and has heard of "north" and "south" poles. In this chapter and the next we shall describe in detail the information available about magnetic poles—and in the end we shall conclude that there is no such thing. I learned about magnetism by hearing this "detective" story in this way, and there are good reasons for my handing it on to you without major changes.

But why, you may ask, do you bother with things that aren't so? Would it not be better to stick to actual facts than to try to teach the mistakes of the past? The answer is "No." We must concern ourselves with ideas that we know have only a limited validity, that are true only "in a way" as well as with ideas that we believe to be "always" true.

For example, the earth is certainly round, not flat. But for purposes of making local road maps or city maps it is much better and simpler and more practical to treat the surface of the earth as if it were flat. When we consider small regions, this notion of flatness is almost exactly "true." We can show on a flat surface the relative positions of five towns in the State of New York with great accuracy, but we cannot show the relative positions of the continents of the earth. For this we need a globe. So, you see, even though the earth is round, it would be silly to insist on making a road map for the State of New York on a spherical surface.

What is true in one area of observation may not be true in another. Remember this. It is a mark of real stupidity (and one which the wisest people occasionally reveal) to assume that some set of ideas that we have found useful and true in our usual surroundings will necessarily be true when we wander "far from home." In some places a man takes off his hat when he enters a building. Never make the mistake of thinking that this custom is universal. In some places it is customary to take off one's shoes. A stay-at-home does not know about these matters, but an experienced traveler does. We are trying to become experienced travelers in the world of ideas about nature. We must be prepared to give up the idea that all creation is made of the sorts of things we think we see and hear around us every day.

MAGNETIC POLES

So by a roundabout road we come back to the subject of this book—magnetism, magnets, and magnetic poles. What did I learn about magnets in my first college course? As usual, we must begin with dry, dull definitions. We must have something definite to talk about. Probably every reader has played with little toy magnets and has observed the repulsion and attraction of the ends of these magnets for each other. In addition to the forces of repulsion and attraction between the magnets as a whole, there also will be torques, or twisting forces, that tend to reorient the magnets with respect to each other. These torques are perhaps most conveniently observed if we make use of a compass needle, which is nothing more than a small bar magnet so mounted that it is free to rotate about its mid-point.

What makes an iron compass needle behave in the peculiar way that it does? What is the quality that differentiates it from copper needles or aluminum needles or wooden needles which are not oriented and do not point north and south? At first it was natural enough for people to think that there was something in the little needle in addition to just plain matter. This something was called magnetism, and since the two ends of the magnet needle behave differently it was assumed that they contained different kinds of magnetic poles. The end of the compass needle that tended to point to the north was said to have "north-seeking" poles in it, while the opposite end, which pointed south, was said to contain "south" or "south-seeking" poles. If you play with fairly strong bar magnets, it is easy to convince yourself that there must be something that might as well be called the magnetic pole present in the magnets and that there are two kinds of polarity. Experiments with compass needles or suspended bar magnets soon led to the observations that like poles repel each other while unlike poles attract each other. A magnetic north pole is attracted by a magnetic south pole; north poles repel each other, and south poles repel each other.

The orientation of a compass needle with respect to the earth's north and south poles is thought of as being due to the presence of a magnet in the interior of the earth, with its ends or poles close to, but not quite coinciding with, the geographic poles. Since we have defined the north pole of a compass needle as that pole which points north, or is attracted towards the geographic north, and since we have said that unlike poles attract each other, it follows that the magnet in the earth must have a magnetic south pole under the geographic north and a magnetic north pole under the geographic south.

We have postulated the existence of magnetic poles in order to account for the forces magnets exert on each other. Now we must try to understand how a scientist goes about analyzing such a phenomenon. This can be done only by making quantitative measurements and attempting to describe these measurements by some kind of law, or formula.

One aspect of any force between two objects at a distance is the dependence of the force on the distance between the objects. Besides magnetic forces at a distance, physicists have to deal with gravitational forces between material objects and the electrostatic forces between charged objects. It would be interesting to discover whether there is an exact similarity between these different forces. All these forces decrease in magnitude as the distance between the objects is increased. How can we describe this relationship between force and distance accurately? We might begin by making a series of measurements of the magnitude of the force between two objects when they are at various distances from each other and simply tabulating the results.

A convenient way of summarizing a tabulation is to plot it, as in the graph in Fig. 5, in which we have indicated forces on the vertical axis and distances on the horizontal axis. Any point on the diagram would specify a particular force at a particular distance. In this graph are plotted four different curves all having the trend which we expect for the force at a distance between material objects: namely, a decrease in the force as the distance between the objects is increased. The four curves in the graph are drawn in a particular way. In the first place, all these curves go through a common point, $r = 1$ and $F = 1$, indicating a force of one unit of strength at a distance of one unit. We might suppose that this was a particular situation in which the force between two objects was exactly one ounce when the distance between them was one foot. The curves now show several possible variations of this force as the distance is either increased or decreased. The curve uppermost on the right is obtained by calculating one over the square root of the distance. Thus one over the square root of one equals one, and this gives us the point $F = 1$ and $r = 1$. When $r = 2$, $F = \dfrac{1}{\sqrt{2}}$, which may be calculated to be 0.707. Similarly, we can compute the magnitude of the force at any distance. If it varies in accordance with this particular scheme, we simply compute one over the square root of the distance. The second curve is plotted according to the formula

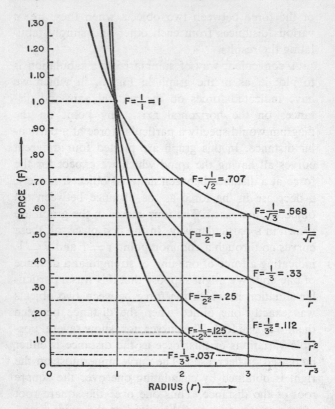

Fig. 5. Forces at a distance might decrease according to one of the mathematical equations plotted here. Measurement of forces due to magnetic poles confirms that they obey the inverse square law, the $F = \dfrac{1}{r^2}$ curve.

$F = \frac{1}{r}$. Here again when $r = 1, \frac{1}{1}$ is 1 and a curve at $r = 1$ goes through the point $F = 1$. However, when r is 2, or when the distance is doubled, the curve goes through the point $\frac{1}{2}$ or 0.5, and for the distance $r = 3$, the curve goes through the point $\frac{1}{3}$ or 0.33. The other curves are similarly drawn according to the formula $F = \frac{1}{r^2}$, or $\frac{1}{r \times r}$, and the lowest curve, according to the formula $F = \frac{1}{r^3}$, or $\frac{1}{r \times r \times r}$. It is now possible to make a convenient comparison between experimental results and any one of these, or any other arbitrary function of the distance between the objects.

Reading instructions and descriptions like that in the foregoing paragraph is dull. However, I remember making graphs of this kind in my early school days. The actual doing of it was fun, and still is. We can draw curves that are not just random shapes but that can be described accurately. Whole families of curves can be contained in a simple formula. The curves of Fig. 5, for example, are all describable by $F = \frac{1}{r^n}$. We have drawn in the curves represented by $n = \frac{1}{2}$, $n = 1$, $n = 2$, and $n = 3$. While there is a certain aesthetic pleasure in thinking up and drawing curves of this kind, there is a further thrill in making measurements on a physical force at a distance and determining whether there is an approximate similarity, or perhaps even an exact correlation, between the mathematical formulae and the physical phenomena being investigated. Gravitational, electric, and magnetic forces have, of course, been studied accurately and in detail.

It is found experimentally that both gravitational forces and electrostatic forces follow a $\frac{1}{r^2}$ law. In gravitational attraction the law unfortunately is very difficult to check with inexpensive equipment. The force of attraction between two material objects on the earth is too small. But our ability to predict the motions of the planets around the sun depends on our assumption of a law of gravity in which the forces vary inversely as the square of the distance, and the success of our predictions is taken as experimental verification of the $\frac{1}{r^2}$ form for gravitational attraction. Electrostatic forces can be measured more easily. We can charge two light objects and suspend them at various distances from each other and measure the variation of the attraction or repulsion between them as a function of this distance, and here again we find that the force varies according to the $\frac{1}{r^2}$ law.

Is the law of force between magnetic poles similarly an inverse square law? The idea of testing this runs into a snag. It is not possible to obtain magnetic poles of one sign separately from magnetic poles of another sign. We have seen that magnetic poles manifest themselves at opposite ends of a magnetized rod. They cannot, however, be removed from the rod, as electric charges, for instance, can. This is illustrated in Fig. 6. Even if we try to separate the north and south

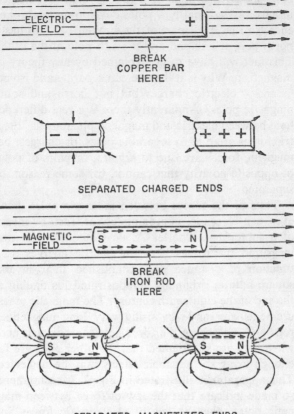

ELECTRIC FIELD

BREAK COPPER BAR HERE

SEPARATED CHARGED ENDS

MAGNETIC FIELD

BREAK IRON ROD HERE

SEPARATED MAGNETIZED ENDS

Fig. 6. Magnetic poles, unlike electric poles or charges, always come in pairs that cannot be separated.

41

poles at the two ends of a rod by breaking the rod in half, we find that new poles develop on the broken ends, so that each part of the broken rod still has a north pole at one end and a south pole at the other. This fact will have to be explained by any theory of magnetism. Why is it that we can separate and isolate + and − electric charges but not north and south magnetic poles? Apparently there is a real difference here between electric and magnetic phenomena. Electric forces are due to separable poles, or charges, but magnetic forces are due to *dipoles,* or pairs of poles of opposite polarity that cannot, for some reason, be separated.

Tests of the forces between magnetic poles, however, can be made, approximately at least, by means of a subterfuge. Charles A. de Coulomb, who first measured the forces between electric charges as a function of distance and established their inverse square nature, originally demonstrated his finding at the end of the eighteenth century. The magnetic measurements are made by using very long magnetized rods and measuring the force between adjacent ends when they are so oriented that the other ends are far enough away so that their effects may be neglected. This apparatus is illustrated in Fig. 7. Measurements so made indicate that the law of force between magnetic poles, like the law of electrostatic forces and gravitational forces, is an inverse square law.

This may at first glance appear to be evidence for the existence and reality of magnetic poles. The argument might be thought to run somewhat as follows: Since the gravitational and electrostatic forces obey an inverse square law, and since the forces between magnetic poles obey a similar law, may we not be justified in assuming that magnetic poles have the same sort of validity in our thinking that masses and electric charges have? We shall see that this argument is fallacious, and that the inverse square law observed in Coulomb's experiment is only approximately valid. In fact, we shall see that it is impossible to localize magnetic poles sufficiently to apply the law rigorously.

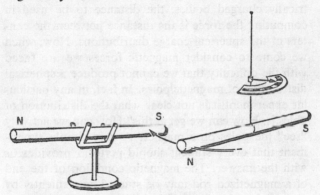

Fig. 7. Charles A. de Coulomb used an apparatus like this in the eighteenth century in experiments to test the forces between magnetic poles. If the magnetized rods are long enough, an approximate determination can be made.

Does this seem upsetting to you? Does the fact that we cannot localize magnetic poles, that we cannot remove them from a rod and put them back again, that we cannot separate them—do these things begin to undermine your first enthusiastic acceptance? It well might do so. These are fishy circumstances. They don't smell right.

43

Let us pursue this matter a little further. If we wish to apply Newton's inverse square law for the attraction between two spherical masses—for example, the sun and the earth—what precisely must we choose as the distance between them? A detailed argument shows that the distance to be considered is the distance from the center of the sun to the center of the earth exactly. Similarly, when we come to consider the inverse square law of force between two spherical, electrically charged bodies, the distance to be used in computing the force is the distance between the centers of the spherical charge distributions. Now, when we come to consider magnetic forces we are faced with the difficulty that we cannot produce a spherical distribution of magnetic poles. In fact, in any particular experiment it is not clear what the distribution of poles is. How can we get at this? How can we actually "see" the poles on a magnet? A very simple experiment that every student should perform provides us with the answer. The magnetic condition of the end of a magnetized rod may be studied conveniently by means of magnetic powder patterns, and this leads us into consideration of the *magnetic fields* in the vicinity of magnetic poles.

MAGNETIC FIELDS

If we put a sheet of paper over a magnet, scatter iron filings on the paper, and tap the paper gently, we shall find arrangements of the powder particles like those shown in Fig. 8, or in Fig. 22 of Chapter IV. In the space outside the magnet there is, apparently, something that has form, a symmetry. It can act on

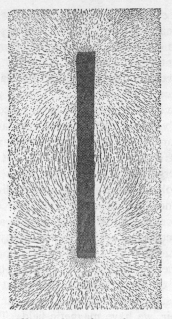

Fig. 8. Iron filings align themselves in patterns in magnetic fields. If you will extend each magnetic field line into the magnet, you will see that they do not converge at a point.

material objects, since it has lined up the iron filings. This "something" around a magnet we call its *magnetic field*. People used to hesitate about saying that a field is "real." When my instructors instructed me, the talk went something like this: "The iron filings are really little compass needles. When we tap the paper, they can turn. They turn so that their north poles point (more or less) toward the south pole of the magnet, and their south poles point toward the

45

north pole of the magnet. The pattern which the iron filings reveal is merely a complex system of lines showing in what direction a small 'compass needle' would point when held near a magnet. The field is just a convenience in describing the magnetic forces at a distance."

Today we are not so sure. The space around objects, the "vacuum" between atoms of air, the region between particles in an atomic nucleus are plainly not just NOTHING. We must assume that the space is full of energy and motion. The atoms in the paper you are looking at are jiggling and jostling in a never ceasing dance. We are more and more certain that in empty space, devoid of atoms, there is an even more complex activity. There are many, many overlapping "fields" which pass energy and mass to and fro, which have symmetry and design, which affect our lives even though we do not bump into them. Out in space beyond atoms, beyond compass needles, and quite apart from the air, we have magnetic fields. They are very real and important. For instance, they are an essential to the radio and television signals that come to our receivers from distant broadcasting stations. These magnetic fields should probably be considered to be as real as stones or flowers, or bread and butter.

Now, what do the magnetic fields tell us about the poles at the ends of a magnet? The lines of a magnetic field radiate from the ends, or poles, of a magnet and then curve away toward the other pole. If the poles were concentrated on two spheres, for instance, we should have a picture like that shown in Fig. 9. Electrical fields like this can be produced. But the fields of a magnet indicate that the magnetic poles

are *always* spread out, that they are smeared out over
the ends of a magnet, as shown in Fig. 8. Consequently we cannot check Coulomb's "inverse square"
law of force accurately.

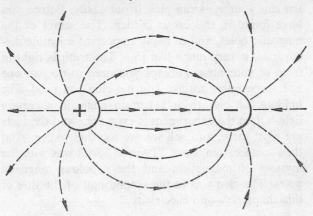

*Fig. 9. Electric fields that look like this can be
produced if the charges are concentrated on two
spheres, but magnetic fields, as in Figs. 8 and 25,
are always "smeared" out over the ends of the
magnet.*

So where do we go from here? In the latter part of
the nineteenth century many people hunted for some
satisfactory way out—some way that would allow us
to see more deeply into the nature of matter, that
would help us to understand these puzzles and at the
same time open up a host of new complications and
facts to study and correlate. The detectives were on
the scent. But they could not see what was plain before their noses.

You have probably seen some of those drawings,

say of trees, in which is hidden the picture of a cat. The trick of finding the cat is not one simply of paying attention, of keeping your eyes open. You must look at the picture in the "right way." Once you have found the cat, your eyes can pick it out easily. Before you have found it, the cat is hidden. The secret of the magnetic poles, and of many important scientific discoveries, is very much like this. The truth is right in front of your nose. Perhaps you need to do just one little experiment to give you the clue you need—like holding the picture at a certain angle in a certain light. Often the experiment is even done and the facts are right there, and still we are too dull to *see*. And then someone sings out, "I see it!" So it was with the mystery of magnetism and the nebulous magnetic poles. The clue was in the second half of the title of this chapter, "—and Electricity."

—AND ELECTRICITY

The actual origin of magnetic fields was discovered in an experiment performed in 1820 by Hans Christian Oersted. This concerned the interaction of electric currents and magnetic fields. Many had surmised that there must be some sort of interaction between electricity (sparks, lightning, currents in wires) and the magnetic phenomena we have discussed. Prizes were offered for a discovery of this connection. For years there was nothing but failure. The story goes that Oersted often gave public lectures, and that in one of these he was demonstrating electric and magnetic phenomena. In particular he had often tested and demonstrated that there was *no* observable

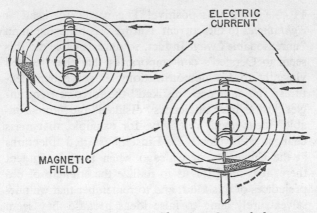

*Figs. 10 and 11. Hans Christian Oersted demon-
strated interactions between electric currents and
magnets with this apparatus. When he held the conductor over or under the compass needle and
switched on the current, the needle aligned itself at
a right angle to the current's direction.*

interaction between currents and magnets. He assumed that if an interaction did exist a current would
tend to align a compass needle parallel to the current. Anything else seemed "unreasonable." In his experiment he therefore set up the compass as shown
in Fig. 10. He expected that closing the switch would
cause the compass needle to rotate. Set up like this,
the result was always negative. But after one lecture
was over, Oersted closed the switch in his electric circuit after the compass needle had been displaced from
its usual position, and to his amazement, he discovered that there was a force, and that the compass
needle pointed in a direction at right angles to the
current. When he set up the experiment, as in Fig.

49

11, the result was positive! The needle set itself at *right angles* to the current. Nature was behaving in an "unreasonable" way! In fact, so unreasonable did this seem to Oersted's contemporaries that they reacted violently to his demonstrations in subsequent lectures. The audience "disliked" the force at right angles, just as later audiences "disliked" the "unreasonable" ideas about relativity; for example, that mass changed with velocity, as Einstein asserted at lectures at the University of Chicago when I was a student there. It is hard for us to realize the strength of old prejudices of this kind, and to remember that we ourselves surely cling to false ideas because they seem "reasonable."

By moving the compass needle around in the vicinity of a wire carrying a current, Oersted was able

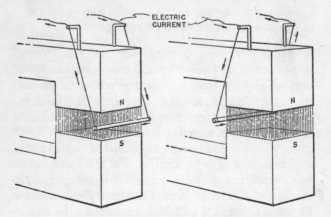

Fig. 12. Current-carrying conductor is thrust sideways when it is suspended in a magnetic field at a right angle to the direction of the field.

to explore the field which it produced. Investigation showed that the magnetic field produced by a current is in the form of circles ringing the wire. A compass needle held near a current tends to set itself at right angles to the current. A first important connection between electricity and magnetism was thereby established. Magnetic fields are produced by charges in motion or by electric currents.

The next step was to show not only that magnetic fields are produced by electric currents, but that the forces which magnetic fields can exert on magnets are really forces on charges in motion, or on electric currents. This is illustrated in Fig. 12. A current-carrying conductor placed in a magnetic field so that the current is at right angles to the direction of the field will experience a thrust sideways. But if this is so, then surely two conductors carrying currents should exert magnetic forces on each other. Take, for example, the two parallel conductors illustrated in Fig. 13. The upper conductor has around it a circular magnetic field which is at right angles to the second conductor.

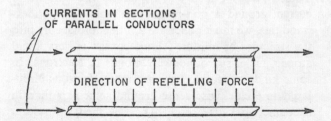

CURRENTS IN SECTIONS
OF PARALLEL CONDUCTORS

DIRECTION OF REPELLING FORCE

Fig. 13. Parallel conductors repel each other if the currents are moving in the same direction. If the currents are moving in opposite directions, the conductors attract each other.

When a current flows through it, there is either an attraction or a repulsion, depending upon whether the currents are flowing in the same or in opposite directions. Now we really are getting somewhere. We have established that moving charges exert magnetic forces on each other. How can we use this knowledge to help to interpret the forces between magnetized bars or magnets? A coil of wire wound around a small wooden cylinder will produce an external magnetic field very much like that of a magnetized iron bar. Further, the forces which two such coils of wire exert on each other are very similar to the forces that bar magnets exert on each other. They behave as if they contained poles—north poles near one end of the coil, and south poles near the other end, even though, as a matter of fact, these poles do not exist. The forces are due entirely to currents flowing in the coils, as can be ascertained by interrupting one or both of the currents or reversing them.

But what connection can there be between a magnetized piece of iron and a coil of wire carrying a current around a non-magnetic dummy? To understand this, we must penetrate a little more deeply into the structure of matter. Atoms consist of very small atomic nuclei surrounded by clouds of electrons. In some kinds of atoms there are more electrons circulating in a clockwise sense around some axis than in a counterclockwise sense. There is then a resultant rotational motion of the electrons around the nucleus. Such motion of the electron cloud constitutes a current, and will produce a magnetic field just as a current in a coil produces a magnetic field. This is il-

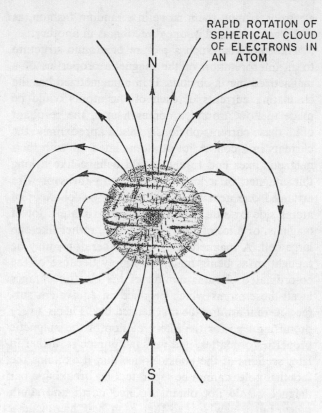

RAPID ROTATION OF
SPHERICAL CLOUD
OF ELECTRONS IN
AN ATOM

N

S

Fig. 14. Moving electrons are electric currents and create magnetic fields even in atoms.

lustrated in Fig. 14. Atoms in which there is such resultant circular motion are magnetic. They are little permanent magnets with external fields just like the fields of dipoles. Other kinds of atoms have no permanent currents and are not permanent magnets. The

53

electrons around them move in a random fashion, as many going around in one direction as in another.

The step from such a picture of atomic structure to an interpretation of the magnetic properties of a magnetized bar is obvious. If in a magnetized bar the circulating currents of each of the atoms could be made to flow around a common axis, the resultant of all these currents obviously would approximate the currents in a coil. A lot of atoms lined up with their magnetic axes end to end would behave like a long thin magnet, or a long thin coil with turns of wire arranged one next to the other. Many such rows of atoms side by side would then approximate a lot of magnets, or a lot of coils side by side, rather like one large coil. A magnetized iron bar, therefore, may be thought of as being magnetic simply because of the co-ordinated circular motion of the electric charges in all these atoms which produce an equivalent surface current around the magnetized bar. This is a very promising lead for the interpretation of the magnetic properties of matter, and we shall pursue it further in later sections of the book. Notice that it explains the fact that poles cannot be separated. By breaking a bar magnet we do not obtain isolated north and south poles, but a new set, so that each half has again a north and south pole. Each half is equivalent to a current-carrying coil, with field lines entering at one end and leaving at the other.

The "detective" story is over. The key to the mystery is plain. There are, of course, endless details to look for and fit into the puzzle. But the main idea which we were wrong about is now at last clear. Sherlock Holmes now can go on to the next case and leave the cleaning-up job to Watson.

OUT INTO THE WORLD

These are things about magnetism that I learned in my college physics courses. Before starting graduate work I decided to take a year off to study physics more or less independently in Berlin, and a very exciting year it was. I listened to many very famous lecturers. I heard Max Planck, the father of quantum theory, on thermodynamics, which I think he loved more than any other subject; Max von Laue, who had discovered the diffraction of X rays by crystals and ran the colloquium where every week new discoveries and ideas were discussed; and Albert Einstein. I well remember the colloquium at which Erwin Schrödinger's wave mechanics was introduced. I took the subway home that night, and noticed Einstein coming into the train behind me. Although I had not met him formally, he evidently recognized my face as having been in the audience that afternoon, because he started right in: "What did you think of that? What a marvelous time to be alive!"

And, perhaps for the first time in my life, I worked really hard by myself. I bought the two-volume, paperback *Theory of Electricity and Magnetism,* by one of its founders, Max Abraham, and studied it from cover to cover. Between bouts of study I spent hours thinking and trying to understand what the book *implied* as well as what it said. I made many good friendships among the graduate students and young instructors and research workers. One was Herman Mark, now a professor at Brooklyn Polytechnic Institute, who wrote an article on large molecules for the September 1957 *Scientific American* that I recommend to you. And there was Leo Szilard of the University of Chicago, who has been a key figure in the initiation of many new ideas, including nuclear reactors and explosions (see the Smyth Report on the Manhattan Project). They were some of the people with whom I would discuss what I was learning, people who would share my enthusiasms, correct my mistakes when I got off the track, suggest books, and point out when my bright ideas had been anticipated years before. I was very absorbed.

One day as I was walking along a busy street, a girl passing me said, *"Guten Abend, Professorchen."* Well—perhaps if it was as obvious as all that, the "Professorkins" might really have it in him to become a professor.

CHAPTER III

Atoms and Molecules

The stimulating experiences recounted in the previous chapter were much in the mind of the ambitious Ph.D. candidate as he stood and inspected the fascinating magnet in the middle of the floor and the big wires and switches on the panel nearby. It would clearly be fun to use it. But how? What should I do? This was one of the very few times in my life when I really was free to choose. Usually when you get up in the morning your work for the day is already laid out. It is determined by what happened yesterday or last week or last month or last year. You are engaged in a project, and in order to complete it you have to do certain things. Even when one project has been finished, a new one is opened up by the results of the first and you are impelled by some kind of momentum to keep on. Sometimes when you open your letters in the morning, you find one that unexpectedly changes the course of your life. There is some compelling need or reason to change your course and do something else. But sometimes, very rarely, you have come to the end of a book and are free to browse around for another. You are free to join the detectives who are off on some particular scent striving to solve some particular mystery. Or you may be free to wander off by yourself for no good reason except that you are curious and wonder what is to be discovered in this or that particular area.

GETTING MY PH.D.

First of all, I made up my mind to measure the magnetic susceptibility of something or other. Roughly, susceptibility means a measure of the force exerted by a magnet on any particular object. The susceptibility of a substance is so defined that if you know it, and if you know the details of the magnetic field around the poles of the magnet, you can compute the strength of the force acting between any particular sample made up of this substance and the magnet. The strong magnet which I hoped to have at my disposal was suitable for measuring very small susceptibilities. You would not use this magnet, for example, to measure the susceptibility of iron. An iron nut or bolt would be yanked right out of your hand if you held it close to the poles of this magnet. On the other hand, substances like aluminum or copper or paper or water have very small susceptibilities. If you hold a piece of copper wire near the poles of such a big magnet, you cannot feel the force. But if you suspend a piece of copper or aluminum or a glass tube full of water near the poles of the magnet and use a very sensitive chemical balance, you can detect the forces exerted.

When I talked these matters over with the professor in charge of the magnet, he told me that he and a student who had just been graduated had used this magnet for measuring the susceptibility of gases. The notion that gases had magnetic properties at first seemed strange, but when I came to think it over, and to read the papers that had been written on the subject, it seemed natural enough. If I hold two bar magnets so that their north poles are close to each other, they repel each other. If I turn one around so that the north pole of one magnet is near the south pole of the other, they attract each other. Why should not the same be true of this big magnet and a gas molecule or atom?

If in the region around the north pole of a magnet a little magnetized atom is so oriented that its north pole is nearer to the magnet pole than its south pole, it must surely be repelled; and, likewise, if it is turned around so that the south pole of the atom is near the north pole of the magnet, it must be attracted. In a gas the atoms bump into each other continuously and reorient each other. If the jostling around due to the heat motion of the atoms is very violent, you might expect the little atomic magnets to be oriented at random and the average pull on any one atom to be negligibly small. On the other hand, at low temperatures when the jostling around is reduced, you might expect, on the whole, to have the atoms so oriented that their south poles are more likely to be near the north pole of the magnets since they tend magnetically to be rotated into this position. The result, on the average, would be an attraction or compression of the gas near a magnet pole. There clearly might be something here to measure. The simplest way might

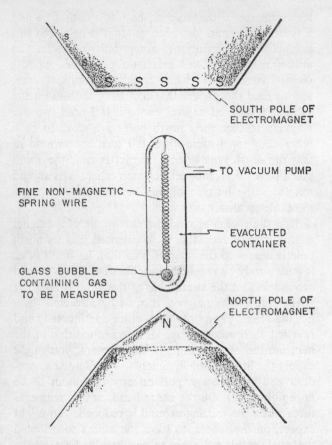

SOUTH POLE OF ELECTROMAGNET

TO VACUUM PUMP

FINE NON-MAGNETIC SPRING WIRE

EVACUATED CONTAINER

GLASS BUBBLE CONTAINING GAS TO BE MEASURED

NORTH POLE OF ELECTROMAGNET

Fig. 15. An apparatus that illustrates how one might attempt to measure the magnetic susceptibility of gases.

be to put an evacuated tube between the poles of a magnet, and inside this evacuated tube to suspend from a very delicate spring balance a small sphere of glass containing the gas whose susceptibility we want to measure. The apparatus is illustrated in Fig. 15. With this we might measure the force of attraction of the magnet for the gas atoms directly.

In principle this is just what we did. There is, however, one flaw in building an apparatus such as illustrated in Fig. 15, in which the force exerted by the magnet on the little sphere containing the gas is measured directly by a balance. The difficulty is that the force on the glass container would turn out to be much larger than the force on the gas atoms. The introduction of gas atoms into the sphere would make a negligible difference in the extension of the spring if the spring were strong enough to support the glass sphere at all. This is the kind of difficulty that one runs into over and over again in designing apparatus. One's first ideas are inadequate, and ingenuity is required to overcome the difficulty. How can we build an apparatus of this kind, in which the force we measure is the force on the gas atoms and not the force on the gas atoms plus container? A possible solution of the problem, and one which has been extensively used, is illustrated in Fig. 16, where we see both a horizontal cross section and a vertical cross section of the apparatus. Four little glass spheres are suspended from a delicate fiber. They are mounted at the ends of a cross and are so placed that because of symmetry there is no resultant torque, or twist, on the glass spheres when the magnet is turned on. The forces exerted on one pair of spheres at opposite ends

61

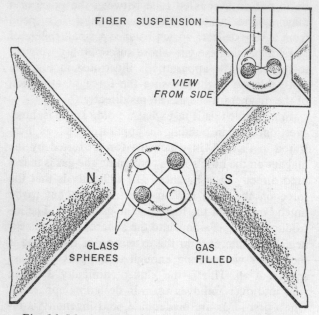

FIBER SUSPENSION

VIEW FROM SIDE

N

S

GLASS SPHERES

GAS FILLED

Fig. 16. More practical apparatus for measuring the magnetic susceptibility of gases has magnetic forces on the glass spheres neutralized. The gases might be introduced into the shaded spheres and sealed off. Or, more practically, the shaded spheres might be sealed off and the gas admitted to the unshaded areas.

of the suspended cross are exactly balanced by the forces on the other pair because of the symmetry of this arrangement. If, now, the gas is introduced unsymmetrically—for example, into the shaded pair of glass spheres—any observed twist on the suspension must come from magnetic force on the gas alone.

Atoms consist of a single heavy nucleus surrounded by a cloud of electrons. Molecules consist of two or more atoms stuck together. Most gases are molecular. For example, hydrogen consists of pairs of hydrogen atoms forming hydrogen molecules. Similarly, nitrogen and oxygen consist of pairs of nitrogen atoms and oxygen atoms, respectively. The chemical formulae for these gases are H_2, N_2, O_2, indicating this diatomic molecular structure.

For purposes of magnetic analyses atoms may be classified according to whether the electrons in the outer cloud spin around rapidly and, since they are charges in motion, produce magnetic fields or whether they do not spin around and consequently are non-magnetic.

Most gases, like hydrogen (H_2), nitrogen (N_2), helium (He), neon (Ne), or argon (A), are non-magnetic. Even if the atoms of which they are composed are separately little magnets (as in hydrogen, for example) when they are brought together in pairs they usually are so oriented that the magnetization of one cancels that of the other. There are interesting exceptions, particularly the bases O_2, oxygen, and NO, nitric oxide. Each of these molecules is a little magnet. I shall speak more of these later on. But Professor A. P. Wills, my teacher at Columbia University, indicated that since most gases were made up of non-magnetic molecules I might as well decide to investigate these essentially non-magnetic substances.

We had better stop here to explain what is meant by investigating the magnetic properties of essentially non-magnetic particles. Substances made up of atoms each of which is a little magnet are called "paramagnetic" or, in some special cases, "ferromagnetic." Substances made up of atoms each of which in the absence of a magnetic field is not a little magnet because there is no resultant spin or rotational motion are called diamagnetic. When atoms or molecules of this latter kind are placed into a magnetic field, an exceedingly slight magnetization is induced in each atom or molecule. This induced magnetization actually is common to all atoms and molecules whether they have a resultant angular spin or not. The induced magnetization, however, is so small compared to the permanent magnetization of paramagnetic atoms or substances that it is quite negligible. It is only in substances that are not magnetized in the absence of a field that diamagnetic effects are observable.

The origin of induced diamagnetic effects is analogous to the action of a transformer. When a current is established in the primary winding of the transformer, a current is induced in the secondary. The induced current in the secondary is simply due to the changing magnetic field inside the core surrounded by the secondary winding. The current in the secondary dies down because of the resistance of the wire in the secondary winding. There is a similar effect in atoms. We may think of the cloud of electrons as being resistance—less windings. When an atom is brought into a magnetic field, there is a changing magnetic field within the atom, and this induces currents in the electron cloud. Since the motion of the electrons in these clouds proceeds without hindrance —that is, since there is no resistance—the induced magnetization is maintained until the field is removed. When it is removed, the magnetization of the atoms

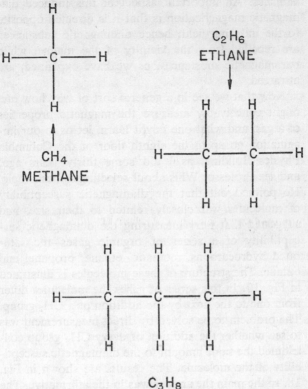

Fig. 17. Shorthand notation for the structure of series of organic molecules.

vanishes. An important aspect of this induced diamagnetic magnetization is that it is directed opposite to the inducing field; hence diamagnetic substances are repelled from the vicinity of the magnet while paramagnetic substances, as we have explained, are attracted.

Now that we see in a general sort of way how one might conceivably measure the magnetic properties of a gas, and what one might learn, let us in our imagination go up to the eighth floor of the Columbia Physics Building, as I did some thirty years ago, and see Professor Wills about selecting a thesis topic. He pointed out that the diamagnetic susceptibility of molecules was closely related to their size, and suggested that I try measuring the diamagnetic susceptibility of a series of organic gases—the saturated hydrocarbons, methane, ethane, propane, and butane. The structure of these molecules is illustrated in Fig. 17. In this series of gases the molecules differ from one to the next by the addition of a CH_2 group. The problem to be solved by direct measurement was to see whether the addition of every CH_2 group contributed the same amount to the diamagnetic susceptibility of the molecule. The results are shown in Fig. 18. In the main the answer was in the affirmative. The addition of each CH_2 group did contribute within the limits of error the same amount to the diamagnetic susceptibility. This sort of result is of great interest to the magneto-chemist, who is interested in the interpretation of magnetic measurements in terms of the details of molecular structure.

My interests, however, turned in somewhat different directions. On the completion of my thesis I received a National Research Fellowship to go to the California Institute of Technology, in Pasadena, to work with Dr. Robert A. Millikan, who had won the Nobel Prize years before for the determination of the charge on an electron. At this point also I was married. On the strength of my wife's being a professional

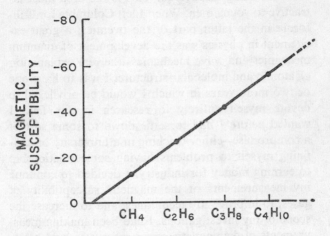

Fig. 18. Two years' work on my thesis is summarized in this graph of susceptibility of the hydrocarbons. The regular change in structure illustrated in Fig. 17 produces the regular changes in properties shown here.

musician, able to supplement our meager income, I accepted the fellowship. We found a little house in an orange grove in Pasadena and set up housekeeping. I started my career as a physicist.

PARAMAGNETISM AND THE QUANTUM THEORY

Physics grows continually. There is an outer edge where new ideas are being developed and where new facts are being discovered. This is the area most attractive to young men. When I left Columbia for California in the latter part of the twenties, a great excitement in physics was the development of quantum mechanics and wave mechanics—the real explanation of atomic and molecular structure. I was to have one or two more years in which I would be privileged to devote myself entirely to research in any field I wanted before I had to settle down to some sort of a compromise—either teaching in a university or confining myself to problems having some relationship to earning money for industry. I decided to continue my measurements of the magnetic susceptibility of gases, to improve my techniques, and to increase the scope of my investigations. I had been making measurements of diamagnetic gases, or gases whose molecules did not have a spinning motion. I decided to go on to paramagnetic gases, or gases each of whose constituent molecules was a little whirling gyroscope, and consequently also a magnet.

The ideas that had been developed by the physicists of the day were really extraordinarily bold and fascinating. Before the advent of quantum theory physicists regarded atoms as miniature solar systems, and compared the nucleus with the sun, and the electrons with the planets going around it. The difference between the solar system and an atom was assumed to be the scale. Here came one of the great errors that men have made all through history—that of extrapolating from truths in one area of experience to another quite different area.

That we were all making a mistake was obvious. We were extrapolating from the motions of planets and satellites to the motions of electrons and atoms. The solar system might in principle have almost any size at all, depending upon how the planets were started in their motions, just as we might put an earth satellite into a small or a large orbit. If we had a very large number of solar systems with identical suns and identical planets but started in motion at different times under different conditions, we would expect them all to move in different ways, especially if in the course of time they collided and disturbed each other. The experimental facts about atoms, however, are that all those of one kind—that is, all those made up of the same kind of sun with the same number of planets going around them—are as nearly as we can tell identical, regardless of the fact that they have different histories and under terrestrial conditions collide violently all the time.

For example, the atoms of any one chemical species radiate exactly one set of colors, and that set only. In particular, hydrogen atoms which consist of a nucleus surrounded by one electron radiate one set of colors; not a single color, but a series of different colors, which, however, are exactly the same for all hydrogen atoms. There clearly is some qualitative difference between an electron and a nucleus on the one hand and the earth and its moon on the other.

The solution to these problems came in the discovery of what we might call *graininess* of many things that we originally thought must be continuous. The graininess of matter was discovered and proved long ago in the nineteenth century. It was shown that gases, liquids, and solids that appeared continuous, like air or water, or a smooth piece of copper, for example, were really made up of discrete particles—the atoms. The discovery of what, for a while, were thought of as the ultimate grains came towards the very end of the nineteenth century and the beginning of the twentieth. Atoms were found to be made up of nuclei and electrons, and though the nuclei of different kinds of chemical substances were different, the electrons were all the same. We since have pushed this knowledge further, and found that nuclei are in turn made up of protons and neutrons, and that, as you all know from reading the newspapers, this simple picture is now being complicated by the discovery of more and more particles. We need not concern ourselves with these. They seem to have little to do with the magnetic properties of matter that we are going to discuss.

The discovery of the graininess of matter and of the fact that atoms are made of nuclei and electrons was, however, not sufficient to account for the observed properties of atoms. Why were the atoms of one chemical species identical, and why did they radiate just those peculiar frequencies or colors that were observed?

Then new and completely unexpected kinds of graininess were discovered in nature. These related to the motion of particles, and particularly to their spinning, or gyroscopic motion—their angular momentum, it is called. According to the best measurements that we could make on visible objects, a gyroscope could spin with any speed that we liked. Its angular velocity could be varied continuously. This turns out not to be so for invisibly small particles, for atoms, or for electrons. For that matter, it is not exactly true for large objects either. There is a smallest amount by which the angular motion of a top can be changed. This becomes observable and important only when we are dealing with very small objects. Any solid object may be at rest, or it may have a certain amount of angular momentum, or twice this amount, or three times this amount, and so on. The different speeds with which an atom has to rotate or spin to acquire these allowed values of angular momentum are very different and enormous. The atom has very different properties when it spins in these different ways. A macroscopic object, on the other hand, because of its size, needs only to move at fantastically slow speed to acquire enough angular motion to satisfy this angular momentum criterion. Therefore by observations on large objects we cannot detect this particular kind of graininess. It is, however, of crucial importance in the theory of atomic structure.

When the rules for describing the motion of electrons around an attracting nucleus had been worked out in accordance with the ideas of the quantization of angular momentum—or, in simple language, the graininess of spinning motions—it was discovered that we had an explanation of some of the baffling things that up to that time had stopped us.

While I was working at Columbia for my doctor's degree, we had very exciting times trying to understand the essence, the intricacies, and the subtleties of quantum mechanics. In particular I remember a group of half a dozen or so of us who met several times a week to teach each other what we had learned. We loved physics and the life in the physics building. There was always someone there, night and day, every day. We usually ate at one of the Chinese restaurants near Columbia; the food was excellent and cheap. We held competitions. I remember particularly a glass-blowing competition, to make a McLeod gauge for measuring the residual pressure in an evacuated glass system. This is a fairly complicated piece of glassware, especially difficult to make in those days before Pyrex was readily available. Pyrex is easy to work because of its low coefficient of expansion. If you finish a part made of Pyrex glass, it generally will stand up even after it has cooled. But with the hard glass with which we worked at that time the story was quite different. Even when you had put the pieces together in the form that you wanted, you had to anneal the material very carefully and let it cool slowly and uniformly. Annealing ovens for this were not available; it was necessary to keep flaming the joints to let them cool very slowly. Even when we had taken as many precautions as we knew how, it was as likely as not that, on returning the morning after having created a masterpiece, we would find it cracked at some vital point.

But what, you may well ask, has all this to do with magnetism? What is the connection between magnetism and the quantum theory and the graininess of angular momentum? One of the fantastic and at the time incredible predictions of the quantum theory was not only that angular momentum could take on only certain definite values, but that a solid object with some allowed value of angular momentum could take on *only certain prescribed orientations* with respect to a magnetic field. Somehow this was even harder to swallow. It seemed "unnatural." First of all, it was strange that a top could spin with only a certain definite angular velocity, but that it could be oriented only in certain discrete directions with respect to a magnetic field was even more peculiar. Of course, these orientations for a macroscopic top were extremely close together and could not be detected. For atoms, however, the situation was quite different. An atom with a single unit of angular momentum can take on only two orientations—either in the direction of an applied field or in the opposite direction. Intermediate values are not possible. Atoms with two or three units of angular momentum can take on additional orientations, but still only a few distinct ones.

With the kind of apparatus I had developed, it was possible to make magnetization curves: that is, to plot the intensity of the magnetization of a sample as a function of the magnetic field that was applied, and of the temperature at which the measurement was made. The predicted results, according to the older classical theory of magnetism, in which all possible orientations were possible, and the new quantum theory, in which only discrete orientations were possible, were observably different. The few experiments which were undertaken, by me and by others, to prove this showed unequivocally that the quantum theory was right.

MAGNETISM AND ATOMIC BEAMS

Much more convincing and much more exciting than these experiments on atoms in gases and solutions was another line of investigation started at about the same time. The experimenters used beams of atoms coming through a system of slits and passing through magnetic fields. The purpose was to study the deflection of the beams by the magnetic fields. The theory is illustrated in Fig. 19.

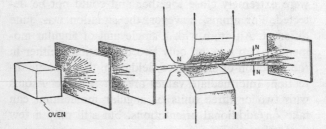

Fig. 19. Atoms are magnets, as is shown by the deflection of a beam when passed through a magnetic field produced by unsymmetrically placed poles.

In a large evacuated vessel we have a source of atoms—for instance, the vapor of a substance like sodium. A narrow beam of atoms coming from the oven is selected by a series of slits. In the absence of any obstacles or deflecting magnetic fields, the atoms travel in almost straight lines to some detector, a photographic plate, say, and the impinging atoms blacken the plate. Along the path of these atoms there is placed a magnet whose poles are so arranged that one is nearer to the beam and more concentrated than the other. This might be a south pole. Atoms in the beam so oriented that their north poles are near the neighboring south pole will be attracted to it. Such atoms will be deflected in a downward direction, but those oriented oppositely, having their south pole near the south pole of the magnet, will be repelled and will be deflected upward. According to the older classical theories, in which all orientations should be present, the spot on the photographic plate should merely be smeared out by the presence of a magnetic field, since all orientations intermediate between parallelism and anti-parallelism to the field should be present. According to the quantum theory, the spot on the photographic plate should be split into two for atoms having the smallest allowable angular momentum, such as the sodium atoms.

The results were in accordance with the quantum theoretical prediction. The spot was split in two by the magnetic field, and therefore it was proved beyond shadow of a doubt that not only was the angular momentum grainy and could assume only certain definite values, but that the angular momentum could assume only certain discrete orientations with respect to the magnetic field.

I was very much impressed by the advantage of working with undisturbed individual atoms in a beam rather than an aggregate of colliding atoms whose observable properties must be some sort of an average which had to be interpreted statistically with the help of a complicated theory. Another way of avoiding the complications of statistical theories was to analyze the light that atoms emit. With very good spectroscopes it is possible to analyze the light emitted by a gas in such a way that the contributions of atoms having different orientations can be separately detected. I was anxious to try my hand at this.

MAGNETISM AND LIGHT

In my two years at Pasadena under the general supervision of Dr. Millikan, I continued to work on the magnetic susceptibility of gases. I made a series of measurements and found that one of the subtler predictions of quantum theory regarding peculiarities in the susceptibility of NO was verified experimentally. I had a chance to do my first teaching and to give my first public lectures. When the second year of my fellowship was drawing to an end, I began looking around for a job and was greatly flattered to be offered an opportunity of staying on with Dr. George Ellery Hale, a famous astronomer and student of the sun, to attempt to measure the magnetic field on the sun by spectroscopically analyzing light emitted from its various parts. This was indeed just the sort of opportunity I had been looking forward to—a chance to study a new aspect of magnetism involving a very peculiar aspect of quantum theoretical predictions.

I began to study the quantum theory of light and the Zeeman effect, as the effect of a magnetic field on the emission of light from an atom is called. An atom that radiates certain particular colors or frequencies in the absence of a magnetic field radiates a more complicated spectrum when a magnetic field is turned on. Each of the individual spectral lines, or each of the individual frequencies which an atom radiates, splits up into two or three or more. The splitting is usually only very slight and requires most sensitive apparatus to detect it, but it is there, and it takes the quantum theory to explain it.

The quantum theory of radiation requires us to get rid of some more prejudices. It had been thought in the days of classical physics that an electron moving around an orbit would continually radiate light at the frequency with which it moved around the nucleus. The quantum theory said that this was not so, but that an electron could move around in an atom at certain given frequencies without radiating at all. The stable orbits corresponding to these frequencies have different numbers of units of the fundamental quantum of angular momentum. In each of these states the atom has a different amount of energy. The state with the least energy—the one in which the electron moves around the slowest—is the stable state. In this state it cannot radiate at all. This lowest state, or ground state, is the one in which we generally find atoms that are not exposed to too violent collisions.

But if atoms are violently bombarded either by collisions in a gas at a very high temperature as in the sun, or if they are put in a vacuum tube in which electrons, accelerated by electric fields, make energetic collisions with the atoms, they may be excited to one of the higher states. In these states of higher energy, or excited states, the atoms do not radiate either, but in making transitions to lower states, or states of lower energy, they get rid of some excess energy and this energy is radiated. A further postulate of the quantum theory is that the particular color or frequency of the light an atom radiates depends only on the total amount of energy which it gets rid of in a quantum jump from an excited state to a lower state having less energy. The greater the jump, the bluer the light or the higher the frequency; the smaller the jump, the more the color of the light radiated goes towards the red or lower frequency in the spectrum.

Though analogies are always imperfect and may be misleading, it may be useful to attempt an analogy of this peculiar behavior of the minute particles of which atoms are made, the electrons and the nuclei. The analogy which I propose will be a room in which there is a flight of steps and a bean bag and nothing else. The room is being continually jiggled so that the bean bag usually will be found on the floor. If, however, the room is violently shaken, the bean bag may by chance be lifted up onto some higher level—to one of the steps of the staircase. Then in the course of time it may fall down to one or the other of the intermediate steps, and finally will reach the floor again.

According to the quantum theory, the color of the light that is radiated in such a jump depends on how hard the bean bag hits the step. Thus, if the two steps are close together, the bean bag will emit reddish light. In jumps to steps farther away the bean bag when it strikes the lower step will radiate light more towards the blue end of the spectrum. For the simplest atom of all, the hydrogen atom, in which a single electron moves around its nucleus, the exact elevation of these steps can be calculated. It is possible to predict exactly from known quantities—namely, the mass of the electron, the amount of charge on it, and the allowed values of the angular momentum— just what the height of these hypothetical steps in the

ENERGY LEVELS ARE CLOSER AND CLOSER TOGETHER
AS AN UPPER LEVEL IS APPROACHED.

*Fig. 20. Energy levels which may be occupied by
the one electron of hydrogen can be represented by
the height of these steps.*

bean bag room are, and consequently just what colors the hydrogen atom should radiate. These are verified exactly by experiment. The energy levels of the hydrogen atom and the corresponding height of the steps in the bean bag room are shown in Fig. 20.

We now can say something about quantum theory and the expected effect of a magnetic field on the light radiated by an atom. We know that turning a little magnet around in a magnetic field requires work to be done. A compass needle tends to set itself parallel to a magnetic field. If we attempt to turn it around we must push on it and increase its energy, the amount of increase depending on how far we turn it. But, since the orientations of the atomic magnets according to quantum theory are limited (for example, the hydrogen atom in its lowest or ground state can have only two), we must expect the magnetic field to split up the ground state into two, corresponding to the energy of the atom when its magnetization is parallel or anti-parallel to the field. Since the energy levels are split by a magnetic field, the frequencies radiated by transitions from and to these levels will be multiplied in number—hence the Zeeman effect referred to above.

ON TO PITTSBURGH

Fascinating as the prospect was, I did not accept Dr. Hale's invitation to pursue these experiments. After living for two years on the modest stipend allowed by the National Research Foundation for its fellows, and in spite of the money my wife earned giving concerts, I was several hundred dollars in debt.

I did not see how in the world I would ever be able to get on my feet again financially. The salary proposed for me by Dr. Hale for working at his solar observatory was, unfortunately, rather small. At about this time one of those letters that change the course of life appeared on my desk. It was from the Westinghouse Company. They wanted someone to do research in ferromagnetism, and one of my colleagues at Pasadena had suggested that my work on the magnetic properties of gases and my general interest in the field of magnetism might fit me for this post. I decided to accept if they would pay a sufficiently large salary. And here I made to myself one of those silly remarks that people are likely to add in such circumstances. I said, "And of course I can always come back any time I want to." One cannot go back. Life does not turn out that way.

To my great surprise, the Westinghouse people offered no objection whatever to the salary I proposed. So, in due course, off I went and started a new kind of work in a new kind of surrounding.

CHAPTER IV

Ferromagnetism

There was a lot to get used to. This was my first eight-to-five job. I missed the privilege of working whenever I felt like it. The long line of cars forming every morning in front of the parking lot at five minutes of eight seemed to me unpleasant and useless. It seemed odd that everybody was ready to quit at exactly 5 P.M. While there was no rule against staying on a little longer, it was inconvenient, and it felt very strange to be in the building, completely empty except, perhaps, for a janitor. The life had gone out of the place, and I got used to leaving at exactly five, too.

When I got up on those chilly mornings in Wilkinsburg, where I had a small furnished room for the first few months of my new job, I was often homesick for California. The chimneys atop the closely packed three-storied dwellings would pour thick black smoke into the street. I thought nostalgically of the California sunshine, of the beautiful orange orchard just behind our house, and of the palm trees along the streets. But when I got to work, things were different. The research laboratory itself was all right. The general atmosphere of the place was not too different from that of the research laboratories at any university I was familiar with, and the people were not too different from the friends I had made elsewhere. But when I was shown the plant in East Pittsburgh where the big machines were assembled and where the parts for the various pieces of electrical equipment were manufactured, I was excited. Here something really new and stimulating was going on. From the unskilled workers who did purely routine jobs, like feeding metal into a punch press, right on through to the engineers who were supervising the work, everyone seemed proud of his special skill and of the contribution he was making to the creation of a new and important part of our life. The great assembly halls were full of a kind of haze, pierced here and there by lights; large overhead cranes rumbled along, raising or lowering some huge swaying object; little electric trains of cars brought equipment down aisles painted on the floor that had to be kept clear for them; people were peering at blueprints; little groups huddled together to discuss this and that point. I began to wonder whether I really knew enough to make a significant contribution, even after a few years, to the design or construction of things I saw around me.

My job at the Westinghouse research laboratories was to learn about ferromagnetism and, if possible, to apply this knowledge to improving the magnetic materials used in Westinghouse products. This opportunity of doing some concentrated reading and studying was most welcome. I went after it with gusto.

There was a very nice little library in the research laboratories, and I spent many hours in it—studying, reworking what I had read, rearranging it, reformulating the statements to try to make them clearer to myself, replotting the graphs in different ways and in different connections, making different comparisons of theory and experiment, until at last I began to get a feeling for the subject, an appreciation of what was reliable and strong, and what were the weak parts of our knowledge.

Then I had an inspiration. Why not write a book? All this material that I was collecting was scattered through many different journals and was hard to understand because each bit was presented in a different way, with different symbols in the equations, and with different hypotheses. No book on ferromagnetism had been written for years and years. A lot of new phenomena had been discovered. The quantum theory was beginning to throw some light on the most mysterious aspects of the subject. It would be useful, and it might be professionally good for me, too. It might help me get back, eventually, into university life. I began to organize the material into chapters and to look for a publisher. The book, indeed, came out in due course, but not until after I had left the Westinghouse Company and had started some new work at my next scientific home—the Massachusetts Institute of Technology. Here is a small sample of what went into it.

FERROMAGNETISM

Paramagnetic substances are made up of atoms that are little magnets. These magnets are free to turn about their centers independently, and because of the considerable thermal agitation of the atoms at room temperature they turn violently. When they are brought into the powerful magnetic field between the poles of an electromagnet, there is a slight alignment, produced in spite of the thermal agitation. As a result of this slight alignment there is a small force exerted on the paramagnetic substance. Ferromagnetic substances brought near a magnet, on the other hand, are strongly attracted. There is an incomparably greater pull.

The beginnings of atomic theory had made it clear that the atomic magnets in iron could not possibly be much stronger than the atomic magnets in ordinary paramagnetic substances. The reason for the much stronger effect was plainly the presence of some force acting between the little magnets themselves, tending to make them all parallel in spite of the thermal agitation, and so making iron a strongly magnetic substance. The mystery was the nature of this aligning force. It was surely not magnetic. In the first place, such magnetic forces should be present in all paramagnetic substances and not just in iron. Further, it was possible to estimate the degree of thermal agitation required to upset the aligning tendency of magnetic forces. It was calculated that the thermal agitation that exists at only a few degrees above the absolute zero should be sufficient to produce random orientations of magnets with respect to each other.

Since these early investigations the behavior of paramagnetic substances near absolute zero has been investigated in considerable detail, thanks largely to the current availability of liquid helium. Liquified gases play a most important part in low-temperature physics. In order to understand this, you might recall that if a dish in an oven is to be prevented from getting too hot, it is placed in a basin of water. The water cannot be heated above its boiling point, 100° C. Heat flowing into it from the oven will cause it to evaporate, but will not raise its temperature. Water is a condensed vapor. Other condensed vapors or gases have other boiling points. For example, liquid ammonia, NH_3, boils at $-33.4°$ C. A dish of liquid ammonia can be used as a constant temperature reservoir at its boiling point. Machines can be constructed for cooling and liquifying any gas, and thus producing a low-temperature reservoir. Nitrogen boils at $-209.9°$ C, and the gas that is hardest to liquify, helium, boils at $-268.9°$ C, about four degrees above the absolute zero, the temperature at which thermal agitation has been reduced to its smallest possible amount. It is found that paramagnetic behavior is drastically modified at a few degrees absolute and this is due to the magnetic interaction of the magnetic particles themselves.

Ferromagnetic substances show a much greater magnetizability than paramagnetic substances. Further, they can retain this magnetization to a considerable extent when taken out of a magnetizing field. Some iron alloys are very good *permanent* magnets. They are hard to demagnetize; others when taken out of their magnetizing field can be demagnetized by gentle tapping. A further point to ponder is this: If there is a very strong tendency for neighboring atoms in a ferromagnetic specimen to stay parallel to each other, then how is it possible that we can demagnetize a sample at all?

An interesting bit of experimental evidence about these aligning forces is important. If they are stronger than the magnetic forces, how much stronger? There must be some temperature at which the thermal agitation becomes great enough to overcome the aligning forces, and to reduce a ferromagnetic sample to a state similar to a paramagnetic sample. Pierre Curie discovered this effect toward the end of the last century. He made magnetic measurements on ferromagnetic samples at high temperatures and found that each became non-magnetic, or slightly paramagnetic, at a critical temperature, which was named after him, the Curie temperature. In iron this is at a good red heat in the vicinity of 800° C. Below that temperature iron is strongly magnetic, but above, it loses its magnetic properties almost entirely. In nickel, another ferromagnetic material, the critical temperature is much lower, in the vicinity of 350° C. These temperatures give a quantitative measure of the strength of the aligning tendencies in iron and nickel. All ferromagnetic substances are characterized by such critical Curie temperatures.

The origin of this force was adequately explained by the German physicist Heisenberg when I was studying ferromagnetism. How can I explain this force to you? I only can describe it and give it a name, and say that it is as familiar as an old shoe to the physicists of today. This force is explained and described by quantum theory, and is the same force that is responsible for other observable effects in atomic structure, primarily chemical and spectroscopic effects. The whole complex of ferromagnetic phenomena, however, is inherently complicated. In the first place, we must consider the geometric arrangement of atoms in a crystal, their interaction with each other, and with the large number of electrons shared by these atoms. The presence of impurities and other crystal irregularities of alloying elements in ordered and disordered arrangements, or crystal grains of various sizes and shapes, and crystal boundaries themselves, must be considered. The difficulty of the required statistical treatment has been overwhelming. As a matter of fact, we cannot explain any of the observed phenomena in precise detail. However, by means of not too drastic simplifications we have been able to show that behavior very like the behavior we see in iron and nickel can be understood. The Curie temperatures in this range can be accounted for as properties of electrons in atoms. Magnetization curves and their temperature dependence can be qualitatively understood, and some of their aspects semi-quantitatively. Even though the details escape us, we therefore consider the basic facts of ferromagnetism as explained and no longer fundamentally mysterious.

The second perplexing point I have referred to concerns the possibility of demagnetizing a specimen in which there is this very strong tendency between neighboring atoms to stay lined up. If we have this tendency for alignment due to the interaction of

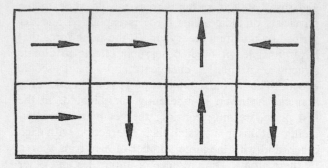

Fig. 21. Demagnetized condition of a normally magnetic material is due to the existence of magnetic domains. They are small regions which have random orientation with respect to the piece of material although their own atoms are oriented predominantly parallel to each other.

neighboring atoms but at the same time we observe an over-all disalignment, then it must be that there are regions or domains within which there is alignment but with a change of direction of alignment from one domain to another. Such a situation is illustrated in Fig. 21. Perhaps the situation is analogous to that in the solidification of a liquid. At high temperatures a substance is a liquid because the thermal agitation of the atoms is sufficient to break down the forces that hold atoms together. They are consequently able to slide around each other sufficiently to produce a liquid. When the temperature is lowered, the liquid freezes: that is, the atoms no longer have energy enough to get away from each other, and they form some regular crystallographic arrangement. Similarly, in the magnetic situation above the Curie temperature the atoms can rotate freely, but below the Curie temperature the thermal interactions are not strong enough to break up the alignment of an atom and its neighbors, and we consequently have spontaneous magnetization and the formation of domains. It may happen that a liquid will freeze into one enormous, single crystal, but it may also happen that it will freeze in some completely different way, with a lot of small crystals such as we would find in an ordinary cake of ice, or in a tightly compressed snowball. We might, therefore, expect that just as in certain circumstances we will have a polycrystalline instead of a single crystal of ice, so in certain circumstances we will have magnetic domains instead of one large single domain.

This hypothesis seems reasonable enough, but I well remember being somewhat dissatisfied with the lack of direct evidence for these domains. One winter evening as I was walking home, I thought to myself that it would be very nice to find some way of making these magnetic domains visible, and it occurred to me right then that this might actually be done. Elated, I began to collect the things that I needed to test my ideas. Within a few days I saw the magnetic domains for the first time.

The idea of how to see them is really rather obvious. Magnetic powders tend to be attracted towards regions of intense magnetic fields. These are often at the corners of magnetized objects. The use of coarse magnetic powders to study magnetized objects to find internal defects in structure already was well known. Examples of such powder patterns are shown in Fig. 22 or Fig. 8 in Chapter II. I proposed

Fig. 22. Iron powder pattern is often used for detection of flaws in magnetic materials. A similar technique can be made to show magnetic domains.

to get some large single crystals of ferromagnetic materials that had nice smooth surfaces and would show no structure with these coarse powders. Then I planned to make very fine powders by grinding the coarse ones, and to have these settle gently on a smooth single crystal surface, where I hoped to see little lines showing the edges of the ferromagnetic domains. If a cross section of the surface were magne-

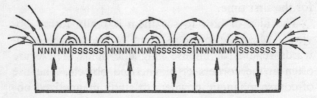

Fig. 23. Magnetic domains viewed from the side should have fields as shown above. The powder should collect at the domain boundaries.

tized in little blocks as shown in Fig. 23, one would expect the field to be particularly strong along the edges of these blocks, and one might further expect the magnetic powders to settle there. This is exactly what happened. One of the early powder pictures that I produced in this way is shown in Fig. 24. The study of magnetic domains by means of powder patterns still continues, and much valuable information concerning magnetic materials has been obtained through their use. I was very pleased, indeed, to have been the first to use them effectively.

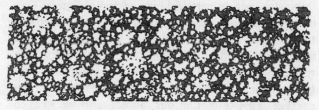

Fig. 24. Irregular domains were clearly outlined in this early picture I made of iron powder deposits.

PATENTS

These powder patterns were interesting enough from the scientific point of view, but they did not help Westinghouse to improve its products. At a series of meetings the engineers explained to us changes in magnetic properties of the various alloys being used in transformers and motors that would be commercially valuable. These were of a great variety. I remember particularly one session devoted to the matter of noise in transformers. A transformer has copper wires wound around an iron core, and there is an alternating current running through these wires. In these circumstances there is a tendency for the iron to hum, and this hum can be very objectionable. I was told that there were particularly vehement complaints from the large apartment houses on Park Avenue about noise from transformers under the pavement. How could we reduce this noise?

Another problem, and one on which we worked particularly hard, was to increase the degree of magnetization that could be achieved in the iron strips that were used in certain kinds of transformers. One of my colleagues brought out a series of records of tests of previous specimens and showed that there were considerable fluctuations—that every once in a while, for reasons we could not understand, we would get a specimen which was very much better than the average. This caught all our fancies, and we went to work to reproduce uniformly the very best specimens that up to that time had been produced only accidentally. All kinds of tests were run on the few samples that accidentally had been good. But nobody could find anything in the good ones different from the bad ones.

Then one day I stumbled upon the answer in the library. Nothing new at all was needed. Iron crystals are little cubes, and, some years before, experiments had been run on single crystals of iron. It was found that magnetization along the cube-edge axis was much easier to achieve than in a diagonal direction. Consequently, if only we could make our commercial sheets out of single crystals of iron with the cube edge along the direction of magnetization, we would vastly improve the product.

This was the kind of tantalizing information that was not practically useful. It was quite impossible to produce single crystals on the scale required. The sheets used in commercial products have to be turned out somewhat in the following way. First, the iron is melted and purified. Then it is hammered out into long bars, which are rolled according to a variety of processes, either hot or cold, until the required thin sheet is formed. From this sheet the pieces to be used are punched out. It seemed quite likely, on the basis of my reading, that the difference in samples had to do with the grain orientation. This could be detected with X rays. The lead which I had dug up was confirmed. It was found that there was not a perfect orientation in the sheets that were used, but a certain degree of orientation, so that in some directions in the sheet there were predominantly cube edges, and in certain other directions there were predominantly cube diagonals. And, sure enough, the best magnetic properties were found when the sheets were used in such a way that magnetization proceeded in the direction of the cube edges.

At this point I began a collaboration with my metallurgical friends. I tried to read up on the theory of metallurgy and of crystallization and grain orientation produced in rolling, and even did a series of experiments. It was fun using new tools and new techniques—rumbling rolling mills that needed a master to control them in order to produce nice straight ribbons instead of a curled-up mess; whirring little monsters for swaging; banging punch presses; great hydraulic forges that could be so accurately controlled that a skilled operator could put a watch between the jaws and bring a great hammer flying down the guides just to the point of cracking the crystal on the watch, and no more; hydrogen annealing furnaces with little red flames at each end, etc. We developed some magnetic tests of grain orientation which for a time proved to be very useful. Little by little we learned how to produce material with better grain orientation, and applied for patents.

As so often happens, progress is made through a series of mistakes. I remember hearing that someone else had discovered a new method of producing better iron for transformers. I looked up this work and found that these patents already had been issued. The patents claimed that by certain metallurgical processes certain improvements in properties were to be obtained. It turned out that these claims were well justified. Among the statements in this patent, however, was one specifying that random grain orientation was essential. This seemed most mysterious. But, on following up the work, we found that although the processes recommended were beneficial, and resulted in a very satisfactory material, a marked grain orientation with cube edges along the direction of magnetization was actually present. One of the tests on which the patents were based had been faulty. These patents were commercially valuable in that they disclosed how to make better magnetic materials, but scientifically unsatisfactory because they did not reveal the physical basis for the improvement.

GETTING AWAY

All this took quite a few years. The depression lasted on, salaries were reduced, long enforced vacations were the rule. During one of these I quit shaving in protest, and when I returned to work my beard caused so much amusing comment that I decided to keep it on, and did for about ten years, until I went into the Navy. No offer came from any university. In fact, most of us felt very lucky to have a good job at all. So I began to hatch schemes. It was clear that the only way of getting out was to become known for excellent work in some field that might be wanted elsewhere. But how to become known? I was doing good work, and occasionally giving speeches about it to specialized groups, but it was pretty slow going. Eventually I decided on two moves. The first was to apply for a Guggenheim Fellowship to go abroad. A year spent in academic surroundings on academic work might enable me to contribute something new scientifically that would attract attention. I collected my papers and sent in an application, and then for months and months there was no answer. Every day when my wife or I opened the mailbox, we looked anxiously for a letter from the Foundation. But no answer came.

The second scheme I had was more complicated, and I am amazed that it worked. I had really become quite an expert on ferromagnetism. I knew just about all the papers that had been written on the subject, and understood them fairly well. I decided that an obvious move would be for me to give a nice long full paper in front of a large audience of important people. But how could such a thing be arranged? The usual papers at the Physical Society meetings were little ten-minute affairs, and as there were many concurrent sessions, you had in your audience only a few specialists. In addition to readings of these short papers, the Physical Society occasionally organized a big meeting to discuss one subject thoroughly. There had not been one on the subject of ferromagnetism that I could remember. Perhaps it was time to organize one.

Such a meeting, I thought, could be arranged, but surely I would not be the invited speaker. No one even was aware that I knew enough to give a comprehensive and revealing talk. So I wrote a letter to a friend who was in many ways the senior magnetician of the country, and suggested that we propose to the Physical Society a big meeting on the subject of ferromagnetism. I suggested that we have a "keynote" speaker. I further suggested that my friend be the speaker, and went on to enumerate in some detail the various new developments that I had studied. As I had hoped, my friend wrote back saying that he thought the idea excellent—the only flaw was that he himself had not read most of these papers. How would it be if I undertook the job of giving the talk? It had worked! The meeting was arranged in Schenectady, and I made a great effort to prepare a good, understandable talk, with lots of slides.

There was considerable interest in my talk. When it was over, K. T. Compton, the newly appointed president of M.I.T., came up to express his interest and appreciation. But that was all. I went back to

Pittsburgh and the daily routine, and nothing happened—until one day Joe Slepian, one of the top scientists and inventors of the Westinghouse Research Laboratories, took me aside after lunch and said that M.I.T. had been making inquiries about my availability. Would the Westinghouse Company consider letting me go or did they want to keep me? Slepian was most sympathetic and understanding, and said that he and many others felt that my real interests lay in a university atmosphere, and that they would certainly not stand in my way.

So, in due course, it all came to pass. A letter finally came from the Guggenheim Foundation offering me a fellowship for a year in England. This year, spent at Cambridge, was one of the happiest of my life. I saw many things that inspired me. I made many friends who showed me a way of life and thought that I had not dreamed of. I returned for a while to the Westinghouse Company, but only for a few months—just long enough to wind up my business there before moving to M.I.T. as, of all things, a metallurgist! I was to be a specialist in the magnetic properties of metals, a physicist to try his hand at understanding some of the characteristics of metals and alloys that professional metallurgists had discovered and used in their engineering work.

CHAPTER V

Stronger Magnets

The strength of a magnetic field may be expressed in a unit called a *gauss,* which, like many quantities in physics, is named after a distinguished scientist. Karl Friedrich Gauss, 1777–1855, who devoted himself particularly to mathematics, astronomy, and magnetism, gave his name to this one. For an idea of what this unit means, we might say that a rather weak magnetic field—for example, that existing at the surface of the earth—is somewhat less than a gauss. The fields between the poles of little toy horseshoe magnets may be as high as hundreds of gauss, or in really strong ones, such as are used in commercial apparatus, a thousand gauss or so. Between the pole pieces of a big electromagnet, like the one I used for my thesis, one might make fields of the order of 20,000 to 30,000 gauss. Fields somewhat higher than this can be produced by an iron electromagnet, but they are not very useful because they are confined to the very small volumes between the pointed pole pieces of the magnet.

The reason for this limitation is not hard to

find. An electromagnet consists of an iron core surrounded by coils of wire. The current in the wire magnetizes the iron and the magnetized iron produces a field at the gap between the poles. In the last chapter we discussed magnetic saturation—the condition achieved when all the little ferromagnetic domains arc pointing in the same direction. In iron at room temperature this is in the vicinity of 20,000 gauss, and it is roughly the maximum field that you can produce with iron core magnets. The slight increase to 30,000 gauss or so is due to an effect that we already have mentioned. There is a tendency for a magnetic field to be concentrated near corners or points. By having pointed pole pieces rather than flat ones larger fields may be obtained.

KAPITZA'S MAGNETS

During my stay in England on the Guggenheim Fellowship, I was planning what new work I would begin at M.I.T. on my return. One project that appealed to me was to make a stronger magnetic field than could be made with iron core magnets. The alternative was not to use iron at all, but to concentrate on the effective use of copper for carrying a current. A current passing through a coil of wire will produce a magnetic field at its center. The larger the current, the stronger the magnetic field. There is no saturation effect here. So far as we know, this increase of field with increasing current continues indefinitely. If you double the current, you double the magnetic field in the middle of the coil. The problem was to discover how far it was practically possible to go. I remember discussing these matters at some length in Cambridge with Peter Kapitza, a brilliant Russian scientist who came to England, became an important part of the scientific community there, had a laboratory built for him, did some pioneering work in developing new ways of producing strong magnetic fields, and then returned to Russia.

The first and main difficulty to overcome in attempting to produce strong magnetic fields by passing very large currents through a coil is that strong enough currents tend to heat the coil, melt it, squeeze it out of shape, and destroy it. Kapitza's solution was to pass currents through a coil for only such a short time that there would not be sufficient energy liberated to heat it to a dangerous extent. This program involved many practical difficulties. Kapitza, however, was not only a scientist but also an engineer. He succeeded in designing novel equipment for producing pulsed magnetic fields of this kind, and also devices for measuring the properties of matter during the small fractions of a second when the fields were reasonably constant and steady.

Kapitza made great progress in developing this trick to overcome the objectionable heating of the coil, but in the end he ran into another limitation, the strength of the coil. You all know that passing a current through a magnetic field results in the application of a force on the conductor of a coil producing its own magnetic field. The parts are squeezed and pushed until finally the coil gives way. It was necessary to build a very strong coil, as well as equipment to produce and switch enormous currents on and off in a very short time.

In the 1930's, Kapitza completed the construction of a most interesting installation. Fields of the order of magnitude of 300,000 gauss, or about ten times that possible with an iron core magnet, were produced in small coils having about a centimeter inside diameter. Not only did he make and operate these coils; he also performed experiments to show how the properties of matter are influenced by strong magnetic fields. Upon Kapitza's departure from Cambridge this work was stopped and was not picked up again until a few years ago.

MY MAGNETS

My own thoughts ran in the direction of producing constant magnetic fields. There are many experiments that are extremely difficult or impossible to perform in a hundredth of a second. I wondered whether one might not design coils having even larger diameters, so that one might put inside them either a thermos bottle with a liquid gas, like liquid air, for maintaining a low temperature, or a furnace for maintaining a high temperature, and still have room left over for experimentation. Questions then arose. How should one wind the coils so that the available power is used most effectively? How much heat could one take out of the surface of a copper conductor by means of a cooling liquid? What sort of flow would be most suitable? What liquid would be most effective? How should it be introduced so that it would not boil away before completing its function?

When I got back to America and eventually to an office at M.I.T., these problems were boiling around in my mind. One by one I set out to solve them. Some led to fascinating bits of research. It is fun to be working on something that seems to you important enough to do it thoroughly, to look into all the little odds and ends that may unexpectedly help or hinder you.

The problem of how to design a coil to give the most intense possible magnetic field with a given supply of electric power is an interesting example to tell you about. First I had to convince myself that this was a sensible problem. One might put it in this way: If one were to wind a coil on a hollow cylinder using different-sized wires for different parts of the coil, was there a best choice of wire sizes? For example, one might use very fine wire for a certain length of the cylinder, then cover this over a longer length with thicker wire. One would end up with a coil having any desired outside shape, in which the current produced heat at different rates at different parts of the coil. Would such a coil give a greater magnetic field when connected to a given electrical motor generator than a coil wound up with wire the same size throughout? The problem might be tackled simply by trying— by using, say, two different wires and seeing whether it is possible to design a coil in two parts that was better than the best uniformly wound coil. It did not take me long to figure this out and to convince myself that an improvement was possible. How then might one proceed to find the very best possible coil? Was it necessary simply to try for the point where any change in the coil seemed to produce a less effective one? Such a procedure not only seemed time-consuming and boring, but it also left the possibility that some quite different design I had not thought of might have been much better.

And then I remembered something. I remembered that in my early days of graduate study I had learned how to find the distribution of velocities of atoms in a gas at any given temperature—the distribution that nature insisted on because it was the most probable. This problem of discovering the most probable distribution of velocities was remarkably similar to my problem of finding the distribution of current that had the greatest effectiveness for producing a magnetic field. It had been solved first way back in the last century in England by James Clerk Maxwell and in Germany by Ludwig Boltzmann.

Now came a few days of real fun—of digging back into the literature, trying to remember or rediscover exactly how Maxwell's problem had been solved, how I might modify the solution to apply to my own problem, and then turn up with an answer, and see whether this answer was practical and how much it would actually improve the performance of ordinary kinds of coils in use. The answer turned out to be not too encouraging. By using a variable-size wire in the construction of a coil, I found it possible to increase the magnetic field at the center by a factor of just 1.52 over the best design for a coil with a uniform winding. Therefore, by going into all kinds of practical complications, one could improve the performance of coils only one and a half times or a little more. However, this now was settled; there was no use worrying about it any more. In the end these calculations did show me a practical way of improving the performance of coils by an appreciable amount.

The next problem was how to cool the coils. How much current could one actually put into the most effectively cooled coil that one could design, and, therefore, how strong a magnetic field could one actually create? I went to some engineering colleagues, got a book on heat flow, and started to learn about the transfer of heat from a solid to a liquid flowing over its surface. The first thing I learned was that a liquid could flow past a surface in one of two ways. For example, water in a tube at low velocities flows in streamlines. Each bit of water flows axially along the tube. If the water velocity is increased, however, there comes a certain point at which the flow becomes turbulent. Little eddies or whirls are generated. Under these turbulent flow conditions the heat transfer from the tube to the water is much more effective. Fortunately, the conditions for turbulent flow were those that I required for cooling the coil anyway. In order not to have the water overheat, it is necessary to push it as fast as possible through the coil, and this means that turbulent flow will tend to occur.

The next point was to estimate how much heat could actually be removed from every square centimeter of surface. And here I ran into a great disappointment. The engineers of that time never had tried to remove a lot of heat from the surface. The data were all for the removal of only small amounts of heat, and the curves describing the quantities to be expected all ended without showing what would happen if one attempted to push things to the limit. It seemed that water would be a suitable cooling medium. What would happen if the temperature of the pipes or holes through which the water flowed was at the boiling point of water, or above? Would steam layers be formed, such as are formed when you spit on a hot stove? No one knew. So with the help of some students and Professor William H. McAdams in the Chemical Engineering Department we set up experiments to find out. We discovered that it was possible to take very much more heat out of every square centimeter of surface than had been recorded in the textbooks on the subject. We found that in turbulent flow any steam layer that is formed is immediately scooped up into the body of the liquid, the steam is condensed, and the heat is transferred to the liquid without the continued existence of the steam layer. An important number for my design was 200 watts per square centimeter. We found that we could take out at least 200 watts for every square centimeter of surface being cooled, and this, it turned out, would make it possible to build magnets far beyond any that had previously been built. Rather than explore the possible limits to discover whether one could go even further, we decided to stop at this point and build magnets based on this figure.

HELP FROM VAN

And so the design of the first powerful water-cooled coils at M.I.T. gradually evolved. An interesting side light at this point was that a thorough search of the literature revealed that actually we were not the first to attempt to build coils along these lines. During World War I two Frenchmen tried to do the same sort of thing. They designed water-cooled coils and found that the only place they could conveniently get the power to operate them was in the private power station of one of the big department stores in Paris. But they had to stop work because of the war, and for about twenty years it was forgotten. My designs were quite different from theirs, and I decided to follow my own plans. Now I was faced with the same problem as the Frenchmen. If we did build some coils, where could we test them?

Throughout this period and up to the completion of the first magnets the chief person responsible for the realization of my ambitions was Vannevar Bush, at that time the Vice-President of M.I.T. He was interested in what I was doing, and gave it the needed backing. To begin with, after I had made some preliminary designs that looked reasonable, he suggested that I try them out at one of the substations of the Boston Edison Company. They had old-fashioned DC power stations which had spare power during the early hours of the morning. He arranged to have space made available for me to set up a magnet, and to get water cooling from the city water mains. And so the first magnet was constructed in the basement of the physics building. It was to dissipate about 1000 kilowatts in a magnet having a volume of about one cubic foot. If the water cooling should fail, the 1000 kilowatts dissipated in this volume would melt everything in it in a few seconds. Our water-cooling tests had indicated that the heating would not fail, that steam layers would not form and stop the cooling processes. But it still was an exciting time. When we set up the magnet at the Scotia Street substation of the Edison Company, the engineers were frankly skeptical. But because of Van Bush's backing they were willing enough to give me a chance to prove my ideas.

I well remember the occasion for the first trial. We were to have the power at some time in the middle of the night, around 1 A.M. Shortly before the appointed hour Van arrived to see how things went. Then, as usual, there were seemingly endless delays. First of all, for some unforeseen reason, the power was not available, and we were told to wait half an hour. Then another hour. Then we went out to get some coffee. I don't remember just how long, in the end, we had to wait. But finally the moment arrived. Sometime near dawn, when we were all worn out with waiting, we stood around the corner of a wall and watched as the power began to be turned up. At first everything was all right. Then there were slight hissing sounds. They got louder; finally there was a bang. Whereupon the power was shut off. When we went to examine the magnet, we could find nothing much wrong. One of the bolts in the flanges of the case holding the parts together had mysteriously exploded. The magnet had failed for some reason quite different from those we had expected.

It was too late for us to do any more about it that night, but we had made some progress although we had not reached the maximum power input into the magnet by a big factor. Then came a period of taking the magnet apart, finding out what had gone wrong, putting it together, trying again. Finally it became clear that there was nothing fundamentally wrong with the design, but that many little details hard to foresee had to be looked after. The usual expression for this sort of thing is getting the "bugs" out of the apparatus. When we got the bugs out, the magnet behaved just as had been calculated. It was a success.

The Edison Company was getting rather fed up with the time-consuming experiments. While they were willing enough to make it possible to test out a brand-new piece of equipment, they were not exactly eager to go on interrupting their own schedules and having their people work overtime on a project of no interest to them. So we called a halt to these tests, and Van set out to find some money for me to get a power station of my own at M.I.T. and to construct some new magnets using the experience gained in the preliminary tests. In due course the money was made available. The sum was perhaps a tenth of what was required ten or fifteen years later to duplicate the installation, but luckily in those days (the mid-1930's) secondhand equipment could be had.

After inquiring here and there, I found that the place to look for big secondhand generators was in New Jersey, out beyond Jersey City. It was a peculiar feeling, going shopping for big secondhand electrical machinery, about which I knew very little. But I found something that looked suitable. It had a central motor, and on each end of the shaft a generator capable of delivering up to 5000 amps at 170 volts. It was an impressive object—much bigger than any magnet I had seen—about 12 feet high and 20 feet long. When I reported my findings to Van, he suggested that we employ a firm of consulting engineers to check on the condition of the motor generator and then to design a proper installation. Perhaps not the least part of this enterprise was to find space at M.I.T. for the installation. By degrees progress was made, and before long we had a 1.7 megawatt (million-watt) motor generator which could deliver power at any voltage from zero to 170 volts. This was very valuable, since gradual starting and stopping were necessary. By means of the voltage control we were able to connect the magnet to the power line without drawing current, and then slowly build up the current and increase the power drawn from the power mains.

For about three years we had three or four magnets in more or less continuous operation, providing facilities for a considerable range of experiments. There were first of all some low-temperature experiments which, as I pointed out in Chapter III, might be expected to lead to particularly interesting results in high magnetic fields. We studied a variety of metallurgical problems: for example, just how ferromagnetism appears in a copper alloy as nickel is added. Finally a magnet was built for the Spectroscopy Laboratory; it was of great importance in helping to explore the electronic structure of complex atoms.

It is hard to guess what we might have done if it had not been for the war. Early in 1940 a letter asking me to come to Washington came to my desk. The magnet work was interrupted for five years, and in that time many things, including my own interests, changed.

New interests always create new stories, some of which I shall tell in the next two chapters. But before going on I should like to add a note to my experiences with the powerful magnet.

Some years after the war was over, and we were continuing work with our battered twenty-year-old magnets, a colleague asked what I felt about the possibility of making even better and stronger magnets. I told him that it seemed to me that our experiments with heat transfer were inconclusive, that we stopped where we did simply because this was convenient though our work promised to make possible a considerable improvement on the then existing art. It seemed that much greater heat transfer might be possible and that if this were in fact so, it might lead to improved designs. In time tests were made, and it was found that at least a tenfold increase in heat transfer was possible without an appreciable increase in the temperature of the copper conductors. That is, it seemed possible to remove heat from the copper not at the rate of 200 watts per square centimeter, as I had designed it, but at approximately 2000 watts per square centimeter. The design of such a magnet would lead to even more critical cooling conditions, and in the event that something went wrong the magnet might literally explode. But such magnets are being built. The bugs are being taken out of the new designs, and more and more powerful magnets are becoming available for scientific investigations.

CHAPTER VI

Degaussing the Fleet

In the last few years of the 1930's my interest in the earth's magnetic field was aroused by a friend who was studying its history. The earth's magnetic field can be pictured somewhat as shown in Fig. 25. The earth behaves as if it had a huge magnet in it. This is very unlikely for a variety of reasons, chiefly that the interior of the earth is too hot to retain any permanent magnetism. Although some scientists suspect that it is due to currents in the interior of the earth that are maintained indefinitely by the earth's rotation, its real origin is still somewhat of a mystery.

MAGNETIC HISTORY

But, you may well ask, how can one study the history of the earth's magnetic field? It is clear enough that one can measure its strength and direction at any point of the earth today, but how get at the past? There are several ways, of which I shall mention two.

Clay is formed by the settling of very fine dust particles in quiet water. The particles gradually are

115

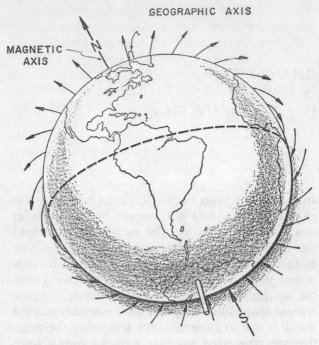

Fig. 25. The origin of the earth's magnetic field is still uncertain, but we can measure the direction and intensity of that field near the surface.

squeezed together, and acquire their clayey consistency. Now, among the dust particles in the air there are always present tiny scraps of iron that are permanently magnetized. As they settle they are oriented by the magnetic field existing in their vicinity, and once the clay has more or less solidified they can no longer turn around—they are frozen in. It follows then that a clay bank will be permanently magnetized,

116

the direction of magnetization pointing in the direction of the earth's field at the time it was formed, provided the clay bank has not been disturbed and reoriented since its formation. At the time I became interested, an extensive program was under way to study many clay banks. The feeling was that if they all gave the same direction for the earth's field at any given time, their story might be trusted, because it would be highly unlikely that they were all turned around in just the same way in widely separate parts of the earth by any local folding or other disturbance. The procedure was to get little cubical samples cut out of clay banks in various positions and various depths, the direction of the cube edges in the bank being carefully determined with respect to the geographic north and south and the vertical. These little cubical samples were then taken to the laboratory, and with the help of rather intricate apparatus the direction of magnetization in the cube was measured, and so the direction of magnetization of the clay bank in the earth was determined. These results indicated rather extensive wanderings of the geographic north and south poles.

Other investigations were also under way to measure the earth's fields at much earlier periods of history—long before the formation of clay banks. This involved measuring the direction of magnetization of volcanic rocks. At the time of their formation they were very hot, and on cooling through the Curie point, they acquired a permanent magnetization in the direction of the earth's field at the time of their cooling. These investigations are still contributing enormously to our understanding of the earth's field.

A LETTER FROM WASHINGTON

These and other investigations I was carrying on at M.I.T. in 1940 were interrupted by the letter from Washington. Hitler's conquest of Europe was well started. German aircraft had dropped some strange-looking objects into the mouth of the Thames. They were evidently explosives of some kind, and probably mines to blow up ships—but an entirely new kind of mine. Up to that time mines that destroyed shipping floated on the surface of the water and were held in place by an anchor at the bottom. When a ship bumped into them, a horn on the mine was broken, thereby setting off the explosive. The new mines were quite different. They sank to the bottom. Brave men, very brave men, volunteered to go down and bring up these objects. They had to take their lives in their hands, since it was to be expected that the Germans had taken precautions that these mines should not be recovered and thus be made to reveal their secret. But some were recovered and successfully taken apart. They contained a little dip needle: that is, a compass needle capable of swinging around a horizontal axis and dipping down to the direction of the earth's field at the point where they were dropped. The needle remained in this position until a ship passed by. The iron of the ship distorted the earth's magnetic field and caused the dip needle to move a little bit. This movement closed an electrical circuit and the mine was exploded under the ship. These underwater explosions sent up geysers that could lift a ship right out of the water and break its back! But I am getting ahead of my story. The letter from Washington was from the Bureau of Ordnance of the United States Navy. It asked that I take a leave of absence for the summer of 1940 to consult with them about certain magnetic problems.

When I got to the Naval Ordnance Laboratory in the old Washington Navy Yard, I found it in charge of a retired Navy commander with three or four civil service employees under him. The same friend of mine who had been working on the magnetization of clay deposits already had been in two or three times to discuss the same problem that was presented to me: how to construct instruments to measure the change in the earth's magnetic field at various depths under a ship. Further, we were asked what could be done to cancel these effects, so that ships could pass safely over magnetic mines. Very sketchy reports were coming to the Navy Department that first the Swedes, and then the English, were putting electrical cables around the outside of ships and running currents through them in such a way as to cancel the ship's magnetization. This was really a process of demagnetizing the ship, but it was given the special name "degaussing," the gauss being the unit of magnetic field, and degaussing being the process of removing the stray magnetic field produced by the magnetized iron of the ships.

—AND A TRIP TO ENGLAND

It was decided that the most useful thing I could do would be to go to England and find out more of what was actually going on. It was felt that my scientific reports based on direct observation on the spot might supplement valuably the reports that Naval officers were sending back. Other scientists might be gathered in Washington at the Naval Ordnance Laboratory to take up the problems of measuring the fields of ships, and of demagnetizing them, using as best they could whatever information I might gather in England.

This was a very exciting time for me. Nowadays major and minor wars are common, universal military service has been established, and everyone feels that he may somehow be exposed to military action at relatively short notice. In 1940, however, we had had almost twenty-five years of peace and disarmament. It seemed risky to go into a war area. The Germans had collected their fleet of invasion boats on the French coast. It seemed quite possible that there would be an invasion, and that I would be taken prisoner, but I was keen to go if there was some useful purpose to be achieved.

Two naval officers and I got special diplomatic passports and a first-class passage on a ship leaving from Montreal. I was a "specialist," to report on technical aspects of mine warfare, especially magnetic mine warfare. The two naval officers were to concentrate on mine sweeping, and on the installation of degaussing cables. On the train going from Washington to Montreal, I remember that a new blue suit was delivered in New York, a contribution from the family to my professor's wardrobe. I was able to stop off for a few hours in Vermont, where my wife met me to say good-by.

When we got to Liverpool we saw the first signs of

war. Ships, broken in half in the middle, lay around the harbor. They were victims of the new ground mines. We also saw the first mine sweeping going on. At first we could not understand it. Tugboats were steaming about the harbor dragging enormous black snakes behind them. These were large cables covered with bouyant insulation so they would float. On the tugboats there were powerful motor generators to produce a current. One electrode was at a relatively short distance behind the tug, the other at the far end of the cable. A current was made to pass from the distant electrode through the sea water in a rather wide circling path to the forward electrode. These currents produced magnetic fields behind the tugboats. The tugboats, therefore, had to be very carefully degaussed, because they had to travel over the magnetic mines without exploding them. Then, behind the tugboats, were the magnetic fields produced by currents in the sea, to imitate the field of a ship.

This seemed at first a rather odd way of producing a magnetic field. The standard way of doing it is to make a coil. One could make much stronger fields with smaller currents by means of coils of wire, but the problem of making a coil that could conveniently be towed behind a tugboat was extremely difficult. This was actually a most brilliant solution, which made it possible to tow much less wire than would be needed in a coil, and to have the wire in an extremely simple form for towing.

Another form of magnetic mine sweeper that I later saw was a relatively large ship carrying a very strong magnet weighing many, many tons. This was a bar magnet going from the bow of the ship, usually near the top deck, way aft. This bar magnet, many feet in diameter, had coils wound around it which passed a current produced by big motor generators. The magnet was intended to produce magnetic fields ahead of the ship, so that as it steamed around a harbor it would explode magnetic mines before passing over them. These magnet ships were never as common as the "electric tail" kind of mine sweepers using currents through the water, probably because they were so costly.

One point to be remembered is that the purpose in laying magnetic mines turned out to be not only to sink ships but to force the enemy to spend enormous sums of money and to use valuable ships and valuable copper in mine sweeping and in degaussing. The incidental nuisance value in closing harbors and forcing the enemy thus to use his resources was perhaps as valuable as the actual sinkings.

At the American Embassy in London, I began reading reports from our British colleagues, and I went to various naval bases to talk to people in charge of operations, some of them old friends who tried to educate me in what they had learned and what they were doing. Because of the very small earth fields concerned and the very small magnetic effects to be compensated for, the magnetism of ships was in many ways different from the magnetism of ferromagnetic objects that we had studied. For some time quite a bit had been known about the magnetism of ships because of magnetic effect on the compass. A magnetic compass needle will point to the magnetic north only if the earth's magnetic field is not distorted. In some regions the field is considerably distorted by ferromagnetic iron deposits. Charts pointing out these local deviations are available, but magnetization of the ship introduces navigating difficulties. As the ship changes its heading, its magnetization changes, and consequently the deviation of the compass changes. Little sets of magnets have to be installed near a compass needle to compensate.

But it turned out that this knowledge was not very helpful in degaussing ships. To begin with, measurements had to be made. In the entrance to harbors coils were placed on the bottom, and as ships came in and out of the harbor they passed over these coils, which sent electrical impulses to recording instruments on the shore. Here the changes in magnetic fields in the coils due to passing ships were recorded on a paper tape. These records were called "ships signatures," and were studied by large groups of specialists. They would prescribe steps to reduce the magnetic disturbance, and after degaussing procedures had been completed, the ships, if possible, would be sent over the range again and a new "signature" taken. Civilian scientists who had become expert in these matters then had to advise the captain of the ship about the degree of safety achieved, or the Admiralty about the desirability of letting a certain ship sail or remain for further attention.

The magnetization of a ship could be considered in two parts. When the ship was assembled, especially when rivets were put into it, the iron parts acquired a magnetization in the direction of the local earth's field. A great deal of this magnetization was more or less permanent, and remained with the ship throughout its life unless special precautions were taken to remove it. This permanent magnetization could be removed by a demagnetization process. The technique for doing this was first developed in France before Hitler took over. Temporary coils were wound around a ship, and pulses of current were sent through the coil until, in a process of trial and error, the permanent magnetization was removed. This process was called *deperming,* or taking out the permanent magnetization, and was a most valuable part of the degaussing process. It is much the same as demagnetizing a watch. If a watch is put into too strong a field, any ferromagnetic parts become permanently magnetized and exert forces on each other. These forces may completely stop a watch, or at least make it run erratically as the parts move with respect to each other and accelerating forces change to retarding forces. In a watch we do not know the direction of magnetization, so it is usual to place it in an alternating field, pointing first in one direction and then in another, and as the alternating field is gradually reduced to zero the watch is demagnetized. Ships are demagnetized by an essentially similar technique, but the effect of individual demagnetizing pulses is observed.

Once the permanent magnetization has been taken out of a ship, there is left the induced magnetization. It is found that when a ship heads north there is a tendency for a north pole to be induced in its bow and the south pole in its stern, and when it turns around the opposite happens. The extent of this magnetization depends on the field strength of the earth's field at the ship's position and, of course, on the heading of the ship. This induced magnetization must be taken care of by degaussing coils: that is, by coils in which currents are passed with a strength depending upon the heading and the location of the ship in the earth's field.

The real point of my work was to help to determine the practical limit to which the complexity of degaussing installations should go. The more trouble you took, the more money and time you spent, the better the job you could do. How far was the United States Navy justified in going at any particular stage of the war for any particular ship? These were the questions which the naval administration had to decide. The job of the technical people was to give an estimate of how much it would cost to do a job of any given degree of perfection.

BACK TO WASHINGTON

When the time came to go back to the United States and we boarded our ship in the Mersey at Liverpool, we found it full of British sailors. Why on earth, we wondered, were they being sent in style on a passenger ship to Halifax, Nova Scotia? We were not to get the answer until the voyage was half over. Before leaving Liverpool we were aboard ship one night, and a very interesting night it was, too. Not a light showing anywhere, either on shore or in the harbor. Presently the air raid sirens wailed, and there was a full-scale bombing attack. To our amazement, not a single searchlight was turned on. This must have been one of the first occasions anti-aircraft was directed entirely by radar. Our ship had several near misses. Some people thought we were a main target because of the British sailors aboard, and the mystery of why they were there became still more interesting.

About mid-point in the Atlantic we heard a broadcast by President Roosevelt. He announced that the United States was turning over fifty destroyers to the British Navy and that they were on their way to Halifax to be taken over by British crews. Of course, there was great excitement. Cases of champagne were brought out and toasts exchanged. For the rest of the voyage the officers in our party spent their time lecturing the British sailors on the construction and operation of our old destroyers. As we approached Halifax several days later, we saw the long line of American destroyers steaming into the harbor. It was a thrilling sight.

On my return to Washington I was asked to report to the Bureau of Ordnance. The officers there were anxious for me and the returning naval officers to describe as much of the actual war as we had seen, before going to our technical duties. I was asked, first of all, to extend my three-month leave of absence from M.I.T. and to delay for some time going back to the Naval Ordnance Laboratory. Actually, my leave of absence from M.I.T. was extended for five full years, until the end of the war with Japan, and I never did get back to the Naval Ordnance Laboratory at all. My work developed along the lines of what was later to be called Operations Analysis. My job was to provide a link between the officers in the Bureau of Ordnance and my scientific colleagues in the laboratory. On the one hand, I was to tell the heads of the laboratory the kinds of things that appeared to be operationally useful, and on the other hand, to report back to the naval officers the kinds of things the technical people felt they could do. We began to study naval operations quantitatively, and to try to estimate the effectiveness of various sorts of weapons and countermeasures. This kind of analysis has flourished in England as well as in America, and is now a recognized and an important aspect of many types of operations in business and in military establishments.

One of our jobs was to design magnetic mines and other kinds of mines for the war against Japan. Detailed statistical information was gathered about the depth of harbors in the Pacific, about possible ways of laying mines, about difficulties concerning storage, and many other factors.

Various new magnetic problems related to our degaussing activities eventually came to light. There was, first of all, the magnetic detection of submarines from airplanes. It would be most valuable if a plane could detect a submerged submarine simply by magnetic measurements. This sort of thing seemed very difficult at this time. The techniques for such operations have been perfected to the point where this now is a standard method of prospecting, not only for submarines under the ocean but for magnetic ore under the earth's surface. I have heard the statement made by experts that from adequate magnetic measurements made in an airplane flying overhead they can tell not only the extent of a magnetic ore deposit but also the kind of ore it contains.

Perhaps one of the most exciting projects that we worked on in our studies of the magnetic properties of ships was the design of a target-seeking torpedo.

If a ship could be detected at some distance by its influence on the magnetic field, might not this detection be used to influence the path of a torpedo so that it would automatically be directed towards the ship when it came within the influence of the ship's magnetic field? This became the forerunner of the many kinds of target-seeking missiles now so important.

So it went—for five long years. Not that it was ever dull. There were always new and stimulating events. But when the war was over and there was an opportunity for me to choose whether I wanted to continue in government work on the many scientific projects or to go back to M.I.T., to the academic life that I had abandoned, I had no difficulty in making up my mind. I went back home to Cambridge as quickly as possible.

CHAPTER VII

Nuclear Magnetism

The first colloquium I attended after the war was a most exciting event. Professor Jerrold R. Zacharias of M.I.T. was reporting on results that had been achieved by a combination of the atomic beam experiments that I already have described and certain most exciting resonance experiments. The resonance experiments, started before the war, in many different forms represent a tremendous advance in the physics of today.

This was another of the very few times in my life when I felt I had a free choice. I could do what I wanted. What would happen tomorrow morning was in no way predetermined by the momentum of what happened yesterday. I was returning to the university after five years in Washington. I had no laboratory. (The magnet laboratory had been dismantled and turned over to scientific war projects elsewhere. It was to be reassembled for me, but that would take some time, possibly a year.) I had no students; I had no teaching program beyond doing my share of the teaching load of the department and, to be sure, try-

129

ing to learn physics again. I did not feel particularly called on to go back to the work I had been doing before leaving for Washington. I wanted to turn over a new leaf and do something different, but something that had grown out of the past. I was ready to be attracted by ideas in a stimulating new field. This was it.

MAGNETIC RESONANCE

You all know, or should know, what resonance phenomena are. If you hold down a piano pedal and sing one note into the instrument, you will find that the set of strings that can emit the same note you sing is set into vibration by the sound waves. The others are not. Similarly, the air is full of radio waves of all kinds of frequencies. How is it possible that you can tune the radio in on some one station? The process is very much like tuning a string. There is in the radio a little mechanism capable of oscillation, and by means of the dials you can adjust this frequency of oscillation to any value you like. It will respond selectively to frequencies that are equal to, or in *resonance* with, its own natural frequency.

There are two specially important things about resonance phenomena of this kind. The particular frequency at which the phenomena occur is, obviously, of prime importance. If you know the incoming signal frequency you can use the resonance phenomenon to determine the natural frequency of the absorbing system. Conversely, if you know the natural frequency of the absorbing system you can use the resonance phenomenon to determine the frequency of the incoming signal. First in importance, then, is this close correspondence between the incoming signal frequency and the natural frequency of the absorbing system. When resonance absorption actually occurs, energy is taken out of the incoming wave and is absorbed by the resonating medium.

The second important thing is the sharpness of tuning. In the case of the radio waves this would determine how close together in frequency two stations may be so that you can distinguish them: that is, so that you can tune one out and the other in. A knowledge of this sharpness of tuning gives important information regarding the construction of the receiver.

The colloquium I mentioned at the start of this chapter dealt with so-called magnetic resonance. When a magnet is placed in a magnetic field, it will come to rest pointing parallel to the field in which it is situated. If it is displaced a little, it will oscillate. The frequency of the oscillation depends on the strength of the magnetic field and the properties of the magnet itself. Atoms and their nuclei, too, are little permanent magnets, and when they are placed in the magnetic field, they tend to oscillate much as permanent magnets do. Actually, the situation is somewhat more complicated. The atoms and nuclei are swiftly rotating little gyroscopes. Instead of wiggling to and fro like a compass needle in the earth's field, they precess around and around the direction of the applied field, just as a gyroscope precesses around the earth's gravitational field. The net effect for our purposes is the same. Each atom or nucleus will have a characteristic precession frequency, or a wiggling frequency, in an externally applied magnetic field.

This frequency is determined by two things, the strength of the field on the one hand and the strength and construction of the atomic or nuclear magnet on the other.

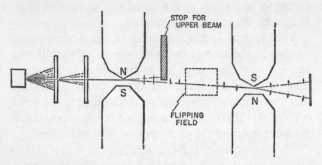

Fig. 26. Magnetic-resonance studies give important information on the properties of atoms and molecules and their surroundings.

The work being reported on had been started by Professor I. I. Rabi at Columbia in the late 1930's, and led to some extremely important measurements —measurements for which Rabi eventually got the Nobel Prize. Zacharias, who had worked with Rabi in New York on these early experiments, was setting up a new atomic and molecular beam laboratory at M.I.T. The general idea of combining atomic beam experiments with magnetic resonance experiments was as follows:

An atomic beam apparatus can select a beam of atoms all with their magnetic dipoles pointing in one direction, and these will be deflected in some one way —up, say—by the final magnet in the apparatus, as discussed in Chapter III and illustrated in Fig. 26. If the atoms are somehow flipped around so that they point down instead of up, the beam will be deflected downward instead of upward and the flipping of the atoms can be detected by the changed deflection of the beam. But the atoms also can be flipped by a resonance phenomenon. They oscillate in a magnetic field, and if an oscillating field is applied, they will respond selectively to the applied field, and will be reoriented. The reorientation can be detected by the changed deflection of the beams.

After hearing this much of the lecture I went off into daydreams and never did hear the end. The thought that had occurred to me was that it might just be possible to perform magnetic resonance experiments of this kind on atoms and nuclei in solids or liquids. The resonance phenomena would surely be there. The main differences would be of two kinds. A new method of detecting resonance would have to be discovered to replace the recognition of resonance by the deflection of the beam of atoms. The second had to do with the sharpness of resonance. One had to estimate something about this in order to construct an apparatus capable of detecting the resonance. The frequency of the oscillating fields and the strength of the constant fields had to be kept steady enough to maintain the resonance condition, or to stay "in tune."

The obvious way to detect magnetic resonance of atoms and nuclei in a solid would be by induction. I have described how a changing magnetic field in the vicinity of a coil will produce an induced voltage, or signal, which can be amplified and detected. Would it not be possible to wrap a coil around the solid in a magnetic field, apply a radio frequency, and adjust this frequency until it was just right to make some given set of nuclei resonate? And could we then detect this resonance by induction effects in a surrounding coil? I decided to start thinking about this.

It was an enormously difficult assignment for a rusty physicist like me. In the first place, there was much about the behavior of atomic and nuclear magnets in solids which I had to look up in the literature. In the second place, there was a great deal more that was not known, but that had to be guessed at, and the whole trick of building a suitable apparatus was in the shrewdness of the guesses about the things one did not know. Before very many days had passed, however, many of my difficulties were overcome in an unexpected way.

I learned that just a few miles away, at Harvard, Professor Edward Purcell and some of his collaborators were actually setting up an experiment of this kind. They had been doing scientific work during the war years, and their technical skill at designing and building electronic equipment of this kind was at its peak. Moreover, they had read the literature on the subject, knew what was to be known, and were making extremely shrewd guesses, as it turned out, regarding those parts of the experiment which they did not know. Within a few weeks Purcell and his collaborators had actually found the first nuclear magnetic resonance. A short time later we learned that still another group, working under Professor Felix Bloch of Stanford University, had also developed equipment for this same purpose, and had also found resonances.

(In 1952 Purcell and Bloch received the Nobel Prize for the work they started at this time.) With the help of two students I hastened to set up an apparatus to duplicate these results, and with the generous encouragement of Purcell, who helped us over many rough spots, we soon also were observing magnetic resonance phenomena in solids and liquids.

My interest in these experiments lay primarily in the possibility of learning something about nuclear structure by measuring these resonance frequencies. A theoretical analysis of the phenomena indicated that the two things about resonance phenomena I have mentioned could be interpreted in these experiments in the following way: The resonance frequency itself gave direct information about nuclear magnetization. It told us something about the magnetic strength of nuclei. This was most important. Theoretical physicists during these years noticed patterns in nuclear properties indicating a periodicity in some ways similar to the atomic periodicities indicated in the periodic tables of the elements, which one sees on the walls of almost every physics or chemistry lecture hall. Nuclei were presently thought of as being composed of a series of shells of protons and neutrons that were particularly stable, with a few outer particles responsible for angular momentum, magnetism, radioactivity, and so on. It was most important to get more and more experimental evidence to help check the correctness of these ideas.

The second thing, the sharpness of tuning, gave information about the nuclear environment, or the structure of the solid or liquid in which the nuclei are situated. One could investigate how modifications

135

in the temperature or in the chemical composition of the material in which the nuclei were oscillating affected the details of the resonance phenomena, and thus get detailed information about this structure.

A group of graduate students elected to work with me in this general area in the years immediately after the war. Some of them followed the direction of studying nuclear structure, while others investigated new effects on the structures of solids and liquids. I myself got an apparatus together and spent six weeks in the laboratory. It was a happy time. In this short period we made measurements of the magnetization of a dozen or so nuclei more accurately than previously had been done. And out of these few measurements came a rather important result.

NUCLEAR MAGNETIC STRUCTURE

Perhaps it is worth trying to explain how this came about. In the end it led to the possibility of measuring not merely the strength of nuclear magnets but also something about their shape—the distribution of the magnetization within the fantastically small nucleus. To understand this, let us imagine that we have two little magnets mounted like compass needles with springs attached, so that we can measure the amount of force required to turn them in any given magnetic field. Let us imagine that one of these little magnets is long and thin, and the other is short and stubby. These magnets are supposed to have the same strength. That is, if we put them into a strictly uniform magnetic field we must do the same amount of work to turn each around. The torque acting on each when it is

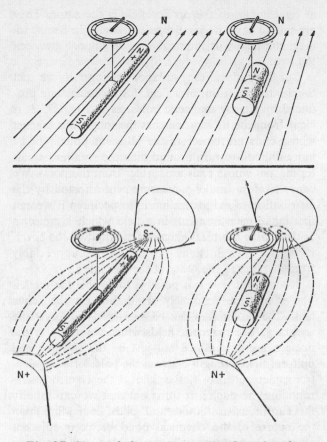

Fig. 27. *Size and shape of magnets affect their be-havior in non-uniform magnetic fields. If these two magnets had the same strength, it would take the same amount of work to turn them in the uniform field (upper sketch). In the non-uniform field (lower sketch) the longer one would be harder to turn.*

at right angles to the applied field is the same. They are said to have the same dipole strength. In a uniform magnetic field it is impossible to distinguish between the two.

But how does the situation change if we put them into a non-uniform field, for instance, one produced by nearby magnetic poles, as in Fig. 27? It is clear from the illustration that the long, thin magnet whose ends are closer to the adjacent poles will be more difficult to turn around than the smaller, squatter magnet whose ends are farther from the poles. We can, therefore, make a measurement affected by the distribution of magnetization in a specimen if we can first make measurements in a field which is uniform to determine the total magnetic moment of the specimen, and then in a field which varies appreciably from one end to the other of the specimen.

It turns out that it is possible to do this for nuclei. The effects are extremely small, but on the other hand, the resonances can be measured with extreme accuracy. The magnetic fields which we apply to the nucleus are determined not just by the average and uniform field strength between the poles of a big electromagnet but also by the field of the electrons surrounding the nuclei. It turns out that we can modify this enormously in liquids and solids, depending upon the nature of the chemical bond between adjacent atoms or, more especially, by making measurements on nuclei in solids, and then for the same nuclei in isolated atoms in atomic beam experiments.

In atomic beam magnetic resonance experiments the energy required to turn around the nuclear magnets of two rubidium isotopes in the relatively nonhomogeneous field produced by atomic electrons circulating around them had been measured very precisely. In my laboratory I had been able to measure the energy required to turn these same nuclei around when the rubidium atoms were in aqueous solutions, in which the electron that produced the magnetic effects in the atoms was removed. Thus we had measurements of the apparent strength in a uniform field and in a non-uniform field, and the results did not agree. They did not agree because the fields were non-uniform. We were able, therefore, to deduce interesting and important things about the distribution of magnetization in these nuclei.

It seemed fantastic. It is difficult enough to measure details of the structure of atoms whose dimensions are of the order of 10^{-8} centimeters. But here, with relatively simple equipment, we were making observations about the detail of the structure of particles that were a hundred thousand times smaller in diameter. It was a challenge.

However, sad to relate, we soon were running out of things to do in this fascinating field. It was not long before most of the nuclei whose moments could conveniently be measured with existing equipment had been measured. The great future of nuclear magnetic resonance experiments lay in studies of the structure of solids and liquids, in attempts to unravel many of the details of interactions between electrons, atoms, and nuclei. Situations that appeared at first to be wholly interactable could be nicely understood with the help of this new tool. New ideas were formulated about such matters as the transfer of energy from one point to another in a solid, about thermal vibrations, about the effects of impurities, about the effects of imperfections in the details of the crystal structure, etc. But the great new field that I hoped to explore, particularly the study of the properties of radioactive atoms, could not very well be approached with this technique. Too many atoms were needed. In order to produce appreciable induction effects in a coil around the sample, a certain minimum number of atoms would have to take part. This number far exceeded the available number of radioactive atoms that could conveniently be made and handled. Some new technique was needed.

BACK TO OPTICS AT LAST

Then I remembered an idea that had occurred to me shortly after Zacharias's lecture started me on this track. How else might one recognize the wiggling of atomic nuclei when radio frequency radiation tumbled the nuclear magnets this way and that? I had thought that possibly the light which atoms radiate might be affected. At the time, various friends with whom I discussed the possibility were discouraging. Since I had been away from scientific research for so long, I decided to trust their judgment without really understanding the reasons for it, especially since the work of Purcell and Bloch had seemed to open up such an attractive field in which there was much to be done without that discouraging specter that always haunts a pioneering investigation: Will it come to anything? Is there something we do not understand that prevents the success of the experiment? But now seemed a good time to reinvestigate this optical problem. In the four years after the war I had had a good chance to learn physics again, and I felt competent to predict the optical effects of microwave resonance absorption. I rashly wrote a paper predicting what one would find, and a devoted and very able French student working in my laboratory, Jean Brossel, decided to try to find these predicted effects experimentally.

It turned out that once more in my life I had made a bad mistake, and it was not just a mistake of calculation—it was a real mistake in understanding. The layman may have a peculiar idea that all scientists worthy of the name know what they are doing perfectly. But life is too short for us to know all the aspects of everything we do. We must be satisfied with thorough knowledge in some parts, and then a certain amount of guesswork and help from others in surrounding areas. And many of us, maybe not the most distinguished scientists but certainly many competent ones, do make honest mistakes that have to be corrected by their colleagues. Within a few weeks my mistake had been detected, and the experiment we were engaged in had to be abandoned. But, fortunately, it turned out that there were different ways of doing this same experiment. Brossel had written about our work to Professor A. Kastler in Paris, who immediately came back with a brilliant suggestion (as a matter of fact, many suggestions) for continuing this line of experimentation profitably.

We now have been carrying on combinations of optical experiments with magnetic resonance absorption experiments in the M.I.T. magnet laboratory for almost ten years, and the field looks more promising every day. We had much to learn both in the theoretical aspects, which were soon straightened out as much as they could be in the light of present knowledge and available time, and in new techniques. Besides handling magnets, by this time no novelty, and handling radio frequency microwave apparatus, which, though new to me, was an old story to many colleagues, we had to learn something about handling radioactive substances and how to produce them in the various available nuclear machines.

In the summer of 1958 we brought in another nice big fish that first nibbled on our line four or five years ago. It took a long while to land him. What our catch has amounted to is this: We have developed a well-known technique which can measure small changes in nuclear size, and we have applied it to measuring the changes of nuclear size of a particular isotope of mercury when one of the particles of this nucleus, a neutron, is put into an excited state. The whole nucleus swells up a little bit, and we have been able to measure this swelling quite accurately. Now it is the turn of the theoretical physicists. How can they interpret this? And further, how can we extend these measurements to similar phenomena in other nuclei to tell whether the interpretation of the theoretical physicists is correct?

As though all this were not enough excitement for one man, I have taken on several other projects. In a sense, I have no choice. Life is in many ways like standing in a waterfall, or so it turned out for me. Either you have the pleasure and the excitement of staying in the waterfall or you get out. I really much prefer to take on the challenge of whatever comes along, provided it really interests me.

So there has been, first of all, the challenge of teaching. How can one be a part of a place full of young people and not concern oneself with what is told to them about the past and the prospects of the future? How can one turn down the privilege of helping to decide what is worth saying and what is not? I could not. So there goes time out of research in the laboratory with graduate students.

And then comes the application of what we have learned. How can one turn down the privilege of going out into industry or government, where what we know is put to work to make things that we want? The old excitement of the Westinghouse shops comes back in an entirely new and heightened way.

Finally, there is the running of the Institute itself. The key to all that I have been talking about in this book lies in the heads and the lives of the professors— the people who for generations have created the knowledge which is a big factor in shaping our civilization. They need a certain atmosphere in which to grow, a certain environment physical and mental and spiritual, too—in which they can function. People who have been around a farm all their lives get a certain knack about when to water, when to plow, when to put in fertilizers to make the fields produce. They learn things that are hard to put down in a book of rules. And so it is with professors at a university. More and more, as your hair turns gray, you are asked for advice, you are asked to sit at long meetings that are not nearly as interesting as it used to be to work in the lab. But it is a great satisfaction to see new laboratories being set up, to see new experiments being started, to arrange for the teamwork that is needed in so many modern ventures. It is important to lend a hand in steering the growth of M.I.T. so that it can hope to meet the challenges of a new generation in a new world.

A FINAL NOTE

And now, after reading this book, you might ask yourself what it is all about. What have you learned? Perhaps it is now clearer to you that magnetism is a subject related to magnets—objects which can exert forces on each other across empty space, forces that are responsible for the useful push exerted by every electric motor that is whirring around somewhere on the earth, or up in the air, or the space beyond it, or down under the surface of the sea. Perhaps you have learned that scientists have discovered various kinds of "fields" in what we call empty space, particularly magnetic fields around magnets, and that we can understand the motion of light from the stars or of radio waves across the countryside only when we come to know something about electric and magnetic fields. Perhaps you will remember that a fundamental clue to our understanding of atoms and nuclei lies in the "graininess" of the whirling motion of the charges which make them little magnets. Do you see that scientists do not live in ivory towers? The scientist is needed in the life of people just as much as the lawyer, the doctor, the businessman, the artist, or the teacher. Have you a feeling that if you examine nature closely enough, and think over and over, and around, and in and out of the facts that experiments tell us about you finally can "see" a most beautiful world that is far different from that which is revealed to you by your eyes and ears? And finally, have you a feeling that the pursuit of science is a most exciting treasure hunt, and that clearly expressed and reliable knowledge is one of our greatest treasures?

INDEX

Abraham, Max, 55
Absolute zero, 86–87
Alignment, 86–92
  of compass needle, 49–51
  of ferromagnetic substances, 86–93
  in magnetic field, 45
  of paramagnetic substances, 86
Aluminum, susceptibility of, 58
Angular momentum, 63, 64, 70–71, 72, 73, 75, 77, 78, 86–92, 131, 135
  and orientation, 63, 64, 73, 75, 86–92
  quantization of, 71, 72, 75
Angular velocity, 73
  of gyroscope, 71
Anti-parallelism, 75, 80
Astronomy, 26–31
Atomic beams, 132–33
  deflection of, 74–75, 132–33
  and magnetism, 74–76
Atomic magnets. *See* Atom as magnet
Atoms, 46, 52–54, 64, 69, 70, 71
  angular momentum of, 71, 73, 131
  bombardment of, 77
  color radiation of, 69, 70, 75, 76–78, 80
  in a crystal, 89–92
  energy of, 77–78, 80, 90
  excited state of, 77–78, 80, 142

  of gas, 59, 61
  ground state of, 77, 80
  heat motion of, 59
  interaction of, 89–91, 139
  light from, 69, 70, 75, 76–78, 80
  as magnet, 59, 63–64, 74, 86–93, 129–42
  magnetic field in, 52–54, 64
  magnetization of, 80
  and molecules, 57–81
  motion of, 59, 69, 91
  paramagnetic, 64, 86–93
  as solar system, 68–69, 71, 73
  stable state of, 77, 80
  structure of, 52–54, 63, 68, 70, 71, 112, 139, 142
  thermal agitation of, 86–88, 90–91
Attraction, 40, 51–52, 66, 75
  of ferromagnetic substances, 86
  of gas, 59, 61
  gravitational, 27, 40, 44
  between magnets, 35, 36, 59
  of paramagnetic substances, 66
  of planets, 27
  between two spherical masses, 44
  of sun, 26, 27, 30

Bar magnet, 35, 52, 54, 59, 121, 122
Beam, atomic, 74–76, 132–33

147